One Summer on The Cut

A Tale of Canal Life in 1964

by

Graham Beard

with illustrations by the author

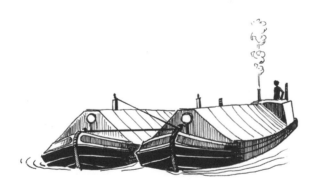

Published for Graham Beard by:
Landmark Publishing Ltd,
Ashbourne Hall, Cokayne Avenue, Ashbourne,
Derbyshire DE6 1EJ England
Tel: (01335) 347349 Fax: (01335) 347303
E-mail landmark@clara.net Website www.landmarkpublishing.co.uk

ISBN 13: 978-1-84306-354-4
ISBN 10: 1-84306-354-9

British Library Cataloguing in Publication Data:
catalogue record for this book is available from the British Library

Printed by: Cromwell Press, Trowbridge
Design: Sarah Labuhn
Edited by: Ian Howe

Illustrations by Graham Beard
Front cover: Harry Arnold, Waterway Images
Inset and back cover: Julie Arnold, Waterway Images

Disclaimer
Canals are exciting places to visit, but can be dangerous.
When you explore the waterways, on the towpath or aboard a boat,
be SENSIBLE, be CAREFUL, be SAFE.
The publishers and author accept no responsibility for any loss,
injury or damage sustained by anyone using this book.

The world of boating families, living and working on the canals, was a secret one, little understood and largely ignored by outsiders. Special skills were associated with it – boatmanship, construction, painted decoration and rope-work, along with the complementary disciplines of canal engineering and management of traffic.

Boating was tough, unrelenting work, an outdoor way of life, bound up with the countryside and the back-yards of towns and cities. It was centred on strong family and community ties; generations of boaters were born, grew up and died on the cut, their lives reflecting the traditions and lore of the waterways.

For twenty years the author has studied this way of life (which lasted into the 1970s) and the skills of traditional boating, often learning from contact with men and women who once lived on the waterways, the last of the working boatmen.

Graham Beard is an experienced boater from Liverpool who has travelled much of Britain's canal system with single motors, pairs or horse-drawn boats. His freelance work includes delivering coal and fuel oil by narrow boat with one of the few commercial boat operators remaining on the canal. Through his work as a volunteer with the Boat Museum Society, supporting the National Waterways Museum particularly at Ellesmere Port, he has learned the traditional skills and techniques of boat handling, helped maintain vintage engines and wooden boats and tried his hand at boat painting.

The Boat Museum Society itself is a community of dedicated people, committed to the preservation of the skills and traditions of the waterways. Its work is both challenging and enjoyable for participants of all ages. The author is keen to pass on to a younger generation the fascination and excitement of being on the canals, and this has inspired the writing of "One Summer on The Cut".

Dedicated to my parents,
Pamela and Derrick Beard

Acknowledgements

I am indebted to Harry Arnold (Waterway Images) for the cover photograph from his extensive and comprehensive collection. Also to Julie Arnold, of Waterway Images, for the back cover and inset photographs, and for invaluable advice and assistance in preparing this book. I would like to thank Gillian Bolt (IWA) for reading an early draft; Brian and Ann-Marie McGuigan (Renaissance Canal Carrying Co.) for the use of their motor; and Joshua and George Hazeldine (Great Nephews) who posed convincingly as Mike and Kit and who have already developed a taste for 'proper boating'.

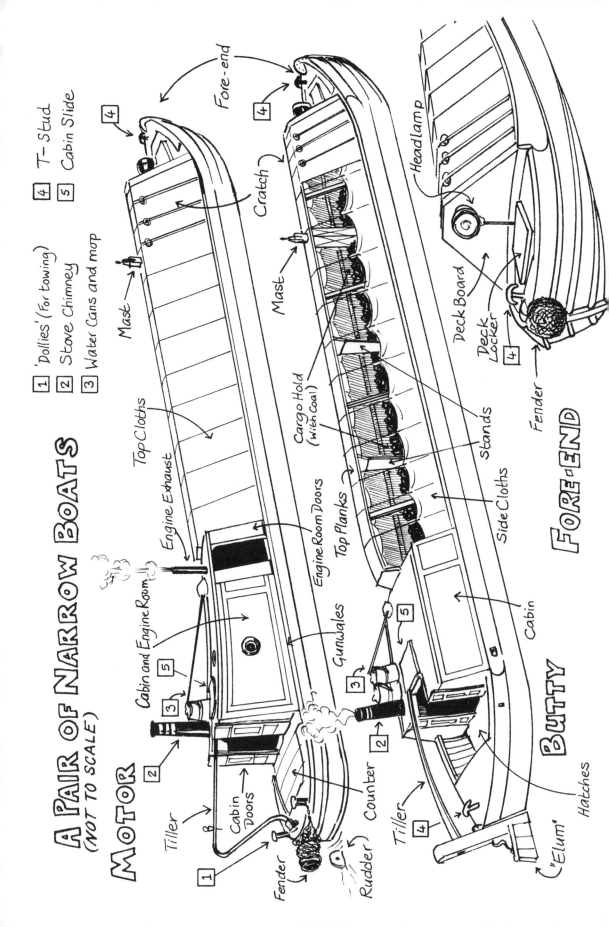

A Pair of Narrow Boats
(Not to Scale)

1. 'Dollies' (for towing)
2. Stove Chimney
3. Water Cans and mop
4. T-Stud
5. Cabin Slide

Motor

Tiller
Cabin Doors
Fender
Rudder
Counter
Gunwales
Engine Room Doors
Engine Exhaust
Top Cloths
Cabin and Engine Room
Mast
Cratch
Fore-end

Butty

Tiller
Cabin
"Elum"
Hatches
Top Planks
Cargo Hold (with Coal)
Stands
Side Cloths
Mast

Fore-End

Headlamp
Deck Board
Deck Locker
Fender

Contents

1. At the Locks

'Go on! I dare yer!'

Mike stood at the end of the rickety old wooden plank, trying not to look down into the murky water far below. He appeared frozen to the spot.

'Go on! Jump, yer scaredy cat!' teased the older boy, who wanted to see Mike miss his footing and fall into the lock.

'You can do it Mike! Go on, 'ave a go!' This encouraging voice was Mike's friend, who was watching from a safe distance. Mike was standing on the foot-board of one of the gates at the end of the old lock. The gates were half-open, about five feet apart. Because the lock was empty there was a deep drop in between, and a cold bath in the dirty water if he fell.

'Go on, yer pansy!' jeered Dave Yates, who could see that Mike was about to take a desperate leap.

Mike definitely wasn't going to chicken out now; Dave Yates would never shut up about it. He stepped back a pace or two on the rotten board that ran along the edge of the gate, before striding out boldly. He ran, leapt, and made a grab for the rail on the opposite gate. One foot landed on something firm, but the other slipped and Mike felt his body tumbling off the gate. He was really scared now, and clung to the rail as tightly as he could. For a moment he swung helplessly, both feet dangling in space. His arms ached like mad, and it seemed ages before he could summon his strength, but he held on. Realising that if he stayed calm he was in no danger of falling, he slowly hauled himself up onto the foot-board, skipped triumphantly across it and landed safely on the other side of the lock. There he took a deep bow in Dave's direction, then jumped in the air waving his hands wildly. His friend Gary cheered and clapped, but Dave Yates just sneered.

'Yah, that was easy,' he crowed. 'A kid of five could've done it,' and tossing the dog-end of his cigarette into the empty lock he stalked away up the canal path.

'Oi! Clear off, you daft so-and-sos,' came an angry voice from nearby. The canal was bordered by houses whose gardens ended at the water's edge. A red-faced man was now peering menacingly over his fence at Mike and Gary.

'Don't you know it's dangerous to go messing about on these locks? You fall in there and no one will be around to get you out. You'll drown your stupid selves.'

The man had more to say, about the canal authorities and the police, but the boys didn't hang around to hear it. They'd been told off enough times before, but it was such a good place to play and they always came back again. Now they ambled off along the dusty track beside the canal, following in the path of Dave Yates whose slouching figure was retreating in the distance.

'You done well there,' said Gary breathlessly. 'For a minute I thought you was a goner, but you really showed that Dave Yates!'

'*I* thought I was a goner too,' admitted Mike, 'but I wasn't going to give him the satisfaction of seeing me drop in!'

'I've got to go now, anyway,' said Gary. 'Me Mum's getting us an early tea 'cause we're off to Weymouth tomorrow. I've got to have an early night, she says, or I won't be able to get out of bed in the morning, and we'll miss the train.' He raised his eyes in an exasperated 'don't-adults-make-a-lot-of-fuss' manner. 'See ya then!' he said cheerily, and slapped his friend on the back. Mike watched as Gary disappeared down a side alley that led away from the canal and back into the town.

Mike carried on walking until he reached another lock. There were several on this stretch of the canal, which ran through the middle of his home town. He often went there to mess about with his mates; but most of them had gone away now. Gary was off tomorrow, then, as well. Now there'd be no one left to hang about with. Some summer holiday this was turning out to be.

Reaching the lock Mike plonked himself down on the balance beam, a massive balk of timber that stuck out from the side of the lock gate. He propped his elbows on his knees, rested his head in his hands, and let his legs swing freely. There was a light wind blowing, which rustled the leaves of the great elms standing on the other side of the canal and played around Mike's legs, which were bare from the knees down. The wind tugged at his dark-blond hair, which was streaked here and there with lighter strands bleached by the summer sun. His hair was too long really, but he had always pretended not to hear his mother and to disappear quickly when she began to shout, 'It's time you got your hair cut!'

Over his tee-shirt Mike wore a loose and comfy sweater – one of several he possessed which had been knitted by his Auntie Cissy, who seemed always to be knitting. This and a pair of old and well-worn shorts were his usual holiday clothes. The shirt and tie, and the green and black uniform of his primary school, were put away now. In fact Mike would not be wearing that particular outfit again because he was twelve and after the summer holidays he had a new school to go to. But all that seemed very far away now and Mike just wished that something exciting would happen to make his holidays more adventurous. But he had no plans himself and, so far as he knew, no one else had any plans for him.

At the start of the holiday he'd gone swimming and played a lot of football, and he had hung around with loads of his mates. Now most of them had gone away with their families. Andy, who lived in the same street, had gone camping with his mum and dad, his two sisters and their great big lolloping dog. The car, with Andy's family squeezed into it and luggage packed in the boot and on top, had driven off early one morning as Mike watched through his bedroom window. The car had jolted to a stop before it reached the end of the street and Andy's mum had rushed back to collect some forgotten item – though from the way the car groaned under the weight of its cargo it was hard to believe they could have room for anything else.

Posh Amanda (*never* 'Mandy') James had gone from a few doors down. She wasn't really a great friend but Mike was glad of her company sometimes. She had gone off in her father's smart new Vauxhall Victor (two-tone green), and had taken great pains to let everyone know that they were *flying* – by *jet aeroplane* – to *Spain*. Well, they could keep their flying and their aeroplane and their Spain; Mike had refused to be impressed. But he secretly longed to be doing something special or going somewhere different himself. Now Gary was going too and there would be no one left.

Mike liked messing about by the locks. 'I don't know what you want to keep going down there for,' his mother always nagged. 'Nasty, dirty place. You stay out of trouble now!' But it was a great place to play. Though the canal passed right through the town it was all hidden away behind the houses and most people didn't know it was there at all. The locks were vast brick chambers with great black wooden gates at each end. When full they looked placid and harmless like swimming pools. When empty like they were now, the wet, slimy black walls plunged into the dark and chilly depths below. The gates were noisy with leaking water, which squirted through them and tumbled into the bottom of the lock where it splashed and bubbled like a constantly running bath tap. If he fell into the lock now, Mike thought, his shouts would barely be heard. And since hardly anyone apart from the boat people bothered to walk along the path between the gardens and the canal it might be some time before he was discovered. He decided he wouldn't mess about any more today.

There was no one else around. It was one of those hot and sleepy August afternoons when nothing seemed to stir, unless cajoled by the breeze. Not far away, from the houses where colourful curtains fluttered at open windows, Mike could just hear a radio playing one of the Beatles' latest hits, 'A Hard Day's Night'. Mike thought the Beatles were the greatest, and his sister Marilyn had several of their records. Marilyn was fifteen and she wouldn't let her brother use her record player – 'you'll only be clumsy with it and scratch the records,' she'd say. But she didn't mind him joining her when she listened to the Beatles, and the Merseybeats, and Manfred Mann, because then she had someone to talk to and to tell how much she loved George, or Ringo, or whoever was her favourite at that moment.

A Hard Day's Night was also the name of a new film with the Beatles in it, but Mike was doubtful that his dad would let him go and see it – 'It's probably full of bad language,' he was bound to say. Mike's dad didn't care much about the latest pop groups; he still had records of singers from ten years ago – and still played them, which embarrassed Mike when his friends came round.

Now the Beatles' music sounded thin and lifeless on the breeze. It was all about movement and rhythm. But nothing moved, and there was not a soul in sight to tap a foot, or wiggle hips, or sing along.

Mike liked being by the water, and when he wasn't getting into trouble messing around he loved to watch the cargo boats which occasionally passed by, climbing up and down the hill through the locks. Mike hoped a boat would appear now; it thrilled him to see them working. More than playing about on the locks, Mike would really have liked to travel on one of the boats. His own life seemed so static; he hardly ever saw other places, only the familiar houses and shops and streets and the playing field near his home. But the boats were always moving, always passing along the water to somewhere new.

Stretching away behind him, beneath the shade of the elms, the canal led northwards. The breeze ruffled its dark surface, sending ripples scurrying across the water, stroking it like an invisible hand. Mike knew that in this direction the waterway wound through the countryside for mile after mile until it reached Birmingham. It probably went further still, on to the distant industrial towns of the North, but he didn't really know.

In front of him he had to shade his eyes against the sun to look at the glistening water below the lock. The bright surface stretched two hundred yards to the next lock down, then on to another before disappearing round a gentle curve, still hemmed in by the low buildings of the town. The water was scattered with twinkling jewels as the sunlight glittered and sparkled on the dancing ripples. This way led down to the Thames at London, to the bustle of the great city and the docks where – Mike imagined – tall cranes shuffled cargoes from the river barges and ocean-going freighters into the little narrow boats. These craft then made their slow but steady progress along the winding waterway, past where he sat now and away on their long journey north. Mike sighed. He wished his chance would come to step aboard one of these brightly painted boats and to be carried beyond the familiar horizon. He longed to discover different places and to enjoy different adventures every day.

A few days ago he had actually managed to talk to a lad of about his own age from off the boats who had come ahead to prepare the lock. He hadn't dared to ask the boy's name but the man and woman on the boats had called him 'Kit' when they shouted instructions to him. He'd had ginger hair and was taller than Mike but his face was friendly and when Mike said 'Hullo,' the boy had replied 'How do?' It had been a brief meeting only, because so skilled were the boy and his parents that they got the boats into the lock, filled it and were away again onto the next stretch northwards in a matter of minutes. Mike had helped Kit to push the heavy beam which opened the gate, and afterwards was left wondering why the boy had spoken in such an old-fashioned way. He had expected him to say 'Watcha!' or 'Hi!' but not 'How do?'

Mike sat lost in thought, a solitary figure in that landscape which seemed abandoned, forgotten, even though it was only a short walk to the busy road and the busy shops, full of people and the hubbub of daily life. Then suddenly Mike was stirred with excitement as he noticed a familiar sound in the stillness. In the distance, beyond the lock behind him, he could just hear the deep and regular thudding rhythm of a diesel engine. Its slow and steady chug-chugging was a mesmerising sound, growing louder and louder, and he knew straight away that it meant a boat – or more likely two boats. For the narrow boats went about in pairs, one with an engine pulling a second craft which had no power and trailed along in the wake of its partner.

Twisting himself round on his beam Mike could see movement in the lock above. Someone was scurrying around closing the great gates ready to fill the lock and let the boats in. The last boats to pass had gone south and had left the locks empty. So the following boats had to fill each lock again before they could pass. As he looked he could see the sunlight catching the reddish-gold hair of a lad at the lock, and Mike realised that this was the boy Kit again, returning after nearly a week travelling in the north. His heart beat faster as he waited for the chance to strike up a conversation with the boy once more – or for the first time really, because all they had done before was greet each other. He watched as the twin prows of the boats appeared side by side in the lock then sank out of sight behind the gates as the water was let out, lowering them to the next level.

Then the boy began to run down the path towards Mike, ready now to prepare the next lock, the lock where Mike was sitting.

2. Boats and Bedsprings

As the boats emerged slowly from the lock above, Mike admired their familiar appearance. All the boats he'd seen looked roughly the same. They were about seventy feet long, but only seven feet wide – which was why they were known as narrow boats. A pair of boats could fit snugly side by side in the locks, and when travelling through a series of locks, as these were now, they would often be tied together so that they moved as one. (There is a drawing at the beginning of this book which shows you what a pair of narrow boats looks like.)

At the back of the motor boat – the one with the engine – was a short D-shaped deck, from which rose the tiller. The steerer who controlled and guided the boat, gripping the long brass tiller handle, stood in the doorway of the cabin which stretched about fifteen feet in front of him, its roof at the height of his waist. Half of this, Mike had observed, was a little living cabin and the tall black chimney sticking up from the roof indicated that there was a stove beneath. At the steerer's feet some steps led down into this tiny space. The forward part of the cabin formed the engine room, and doors on each side of it were open so that the green-painted engine, with its pipes and taps of polished copper and brass, could be seen as well as heard. The engine had its own exhaust chimney, and clouds of pale blue smoke puffed out in regular bursts. In front of the cabin was the long cargo hold, filled today with coal. The coal was only half-covered over with oily-black sheeting, and on top of it were laid long planks on which you could walk to the front of the boat. The cargo hold ended in a little triangular wooden gable, like the end of a tiny house. In front of this were a small deck and the thick iron stem at the prow of the boat. The stem was protected by a knotted rope fender, which cushioned it from bumps.

Beside the motor boat lay its unpowered companion. Without an engine compartment its cabin was slightly different, being shorter, broader and lower. At the back was a large wooden rudder with a long, curving tiller. The steerer at the tiller stood down in the hatches, a small deck surrounded by the sides of the boat. Together the two cabins of these boats provided all the accommodation that was available for the family who operated them. In these tiny spaces they cooked and slept and kept all their belongings.

The boats were mostly black and a bit battered, but the cabins were brightly painted in blue and yellow and were remarkably clean and shiny. Each black chimney was bound with three brass rings, so highly polished that they dazzled when the sunlight caught them. On a long blue panel on the side of each cabin were the words 'BRITISH WATERWAYS' in large yellow capital letters, set in a broad curve. The motor boat had its name, *Cepheus*, in smaller letters beneath. The other boat's name, *Andromeda*, was painted in handsome plain letters that curved along the stern to the point where it met the large rudder.

Mike took all this in at a glance, though for a moment he wondered about the strange name *Cepheus*. He knew that Andromeda was one of the constellations, because he had studied astronomy a bit at school. But before he could reflect further Kit hurried up to him. He wasn't panting as if out of breath, but calmly and efficiently set about the job that he had obviously done hundreds of times before, and which had made him very fit. Mike seized his chance, and leaping to his feet he approached the boy.

'Hullo,' he shouted.

'How do?' said the boy, without looking at who had addressed him.

'D'you mind if I help you?' said Mike.

'Can if yer want,' said the boy, briefly and still not giving Mike a glance. 'You can shut that bottom gate for us, please,' he said, nodding his head in the direction of the beam that Mike had just been sitting on. Then he skipped nimbly over the closed gates at the upper end of the lock where the water was level with him on one side, and the yawning depths of the empty lock lay perilously on the other.

The boy ran the length of the lock and closed the gate opposite the one which Mike was now heaving on. Two great wooden posts banged together as they met in the middle, and the iron gear on the gates rattled in complaint. Mike had strained to close his gate and he stood for a moment with his back resting on the beam; but his companion was already back at the further end of the lock. He suddenly produced – apparently from nowhere – a large, shiny, L-shaped handle, which he deftly slotted onto the gear shaft of the gate, and began to wind. Immediately a powerful cascade of water thundered into the deep chamber, its deafening roar echoing all around the lock which had been so still and quiet. As soon as the water was running he was across the gates and opening the sluice on Mike's side, till the lock was rapidly filling with thousands of gallons of foaming water. And at this point the boy himself finally stopped still for a moment and leaned on the beam of the gate.

He was a little taller than Mike, and very slim, but with the sleeves of his light-blue cotton shirt rolled up above his elbows it was clear that he was strong and wiry. His red-gold hair was clipped short at the back and sides and combed forward on top. Above his brow a rogue tuft of hair stood up straight. His skin was pale, though he must have spent much of his time in the sun; and many freckles stood out plainly above his nose and cheeks. He wore long black trousers, which fitted rather loosely and might once have belonged to someone older and larger than himself; but they were secured at his slim waist with a broad leather belt. On his feet were stout black boots, shod with iron studs that could be heard scraping as he idly swung his foot to and fro on the stonework of the lock-side. The filling lock granted the boy a few moments' rest from his busy task and he simply gazed into the rising water with a far-away expression on his face. Mike approached him.

'I'm Mike,' he said. 'Do you live on these boats?'

'Live on 'em, and work on 'em,' the boy replied, looking at Mike for the first time and fixing him with his blue eyes.

Mike was impressed and a little surprised that someone not much older than himself could be working already. 'What's your name?' he ventured. 'I thought I heard them call you Kit.'

'Me name's Christopher,' said the boy. 'But everyone calls me Kit. 'Cause it's shorter and easier, I s'pose.'

'Where are you going?'

'Down to London. We drops this load off at the factory on the way, then on to the docks to pick up some wood or some tubes, or anyfing they've got for us.'

'Do you like working on the boats?'

'It don't matter what I like!' the boy laughed. 'It's what me mum and dad do. It's the only life I've ever known, and I don't mind it. It's a bit bad in the wintertime though, 'specially if we get iced up.'

'I'd love to have a go on a boat,' Mike said, wistfully, ignoring the remark about ice. The other boy laughed again. 'I bet you wouldn't after a couple of trips! It looks great now, in the sunshine, an' in a nice place like this. But we goes through some really rough places, an' some dirty places, and when the wevver's bad you start thinking how nice it'd be to move into a warm 'ouse wiv a telly, an' a bathroom an' everything.'

'Would you really like that?' asked Mike doubtfully. The boy paused for a moment, looked at his feet, and then lifted his head and seemed to smile up at the trees and into the sky. This great outdoors was his home, and he thrived in it. 'Nope,' he said at last, then added, 'but I might 'ave to, before long. Me dad says that the work on the cut's coming to an end, and loads are harder an' harder to get. We might have to finish up, one day soon.'

'On the cut?' Mike queried.

'On the water, on the canal,' Kit explained. 'We always calls it "The Cut". It was sort of cut out of the land, you see. Loads of men with shovels dug all this, over a hundred years ago. Our Vince's already talkin' about leaving, though,' he continued, returning to the subject. 'He says there's no future in boating. He wants to be a motorbike mechanic.'

'Is Vince your brother?' asked Mike.

'Yeah, he's steering the boats just now.'

Mike had almost forgotten the boats, and he had lots more questions he was keen to ask. But the lock was now full, and with the water levels equal the top gates were beginning to drift open of their own accord. Kit quickly darted across them and began to push the farther one wide open. Mike did the same on his side. But instead of advancing quickly into the open lock the pair of boats still held back, lingering in the stretch of water above.

'Come 'ead!' shouted Kit to his brother.

'Got a load on the blades!' came a voice in reply. It was a deeper voice than Kit's, but not a man's voice. Then Vince's head and shoulders appeared above the cabin top at the far end of *Cepheus* and Mike saw a tall dark-haired lad who, even in the hot afternoon, was wearing a black leather jacket over his white tee-shirt. He was about sixteen or seventeen and his hair, shiny with Brylcreem, was slicked back over his head.

'He's got summat stuck on the prop,' explained Kit. 'It'll hold us up now until we can get it off – and me dad's not here.' With the gates wide open Kit was now cut off on his side of the lock. He ran back to the bottom end and over the gates there, then back up to where Mike stood.

'Come an' 'ave a look!' he shouted to Mike, slapping him encouragingly on the shoulder as he rushed past. 'We might 'ave to help.'

Mike, filled with excitement, hurried after his new friend. As they drew level with the sterns of the boats they could see that Vince had lifted from the cabin roof a long pole with a hook on the end. Leaping across to the other boat, he began to fish around the back end of the motor boat with the shaft, at the place where Mike supposed the propeller blades must be. A woman emerged from the cabin behind Vince, and Mike guessed that this was the boys' mother. She was quite young-looking, with a gentle face and red hair like Kit, which was piled on top of her head, away from her neck. She wore a light cotton frock with a floral pattern, and a lemon-coloured cardigan, and stood with her hands on her hips.

'Trouble?' she asked her son. Vince was getting rather red in the face, straining to reach whatever it was that clung to the blades.

'Here, hold this a mo,' he said to his mum, passing her the shaft of the boat hook. He then stripped off his jacket and laid it carefully on the roof of the cabin. Next he returned to his steering position and fiddled with the controls of the engine, running it hard in reverse. Muddy water churned up around the stern of the boat as Vince tried to loosen the obstacle, then taking the shaft from his mother he began prodding and coaxing around the stern again.

The boats, carried by the breeze, drifted in towards the bank. When they were within reach Kit took a thick rope attached to a rail on the cabin and held the boats firmly. Vince hopped off with the short shaft. From the path he was able to get a steadier grip on whatever was so firmly wrapped around the blades. Gradually, as he pulled, a twisted tangle of thick wire began to appear above the water.

'It's bedsprings again!' shouted Vince to his mother, and sure enough Mike could now make out the mangled skeleton of an old mattress. Rubbish which somebody had carelessly discarded in the canal was delaying this family, and causing them a lot of extra work and trouble. Mike began to feel guilty about the odd things he had thoughtlessly thrown into the canal, though nothing so large as this. He wondered how often the boats got tangled up with nasty refuse, lurking beneath the surface.

With a few more firm twists and turns on the shaft and one sharp tug, the springs finally came free of the blades and Vince fell back onto the grass. But a loose length of the dripping rusty wire had suddenly whipped out, slashing Vince's arm as he fell, and blood was soon running freely down his arm from the gash. He didn't cry out, but muttered something unrepeatable under his breath. His mother looked really anxious though, and climbed swiftly across the motor boat to the path to inspect the wound.

'It's pretty bad, Vincent,' she said. 'You'll have to go to the doctor's.'

'It's nuffink, mum. Don't fuss,' he replied. But he looked uneasy himself. He had pulled out his handkerchief and was holding it round his forearm, but the white cotton was reddening by the moment as the blood soaked through. 'Get the first aid box, quick!' he said to his brother.

'I'll get my mum!' Mike shouted suddenly. The others all looked round at him in surprise. Vince and his mum had never seen him before, and Kit had almost forgotten that Mike was there.

'She's in the Saint John's Ambulance,' he explained. 'She'll sort it out – she's got all the proper bandages and splints and everything.' Not waiting for a reply he shot off down the path and swerved into the narrow alley between the houses, scattering a couple of terrified cats that had been lazing there quietly. At the other end he ran out into the street, turned a couple of corners and was home.

3. First Aid and an Invitation

'Mum!' shouted Mike as he clattered in at the back door. The twin-tub washing machine was thrashing about, and clouds of fragrant steam filled the air. But the kitchen was deserted.

'Out here!' cried a voice from the garden. He dashed out again to find his mother hanging washing on the line.

'You'll have to come quick, Mum! There's a lad on the canal's hurt himself. He's got a bad cut. You can fix it can't you Mum?'

'Calm down, Michael,' his mother said. 'I'll come. Just explain clearly what's the matter.'

Mike told the story briefly and described Vince's injury. Meanwhile his mother carefully checked the contents of her black St John's Ambulance bag, and then she set off with the excited Mike to the canal path where they soon reached the boats.

Vince's mum had found a first aid kit, but it lacked bandages and she was getting a little flustered. 'How d'you do, missus?' she said to Mike's mother. 'I'd be obliged if you'd have a look and see if you can do anything.'

Calmly Mike's mother inspected Vince's cut. She poured disinfectant from a bottle onto cotton wool and he winced as she dabbed it on his arm.

'It needs a good clean, and you'll need to get a tetanus jab if you haven't had one recently,' she said to the boy. 'But it's a clean cut and should bandage all right.'

Within a few minutes Vince's forearm had been expertly cleaned and dressed with lint and a bright white bandage, neatly wound and firmly fixed with a safety pin. There was a strong smell of disinfectant and antiseptic cream.

'You'll live!' Mike's mother declared brightly to the teenager, who was still trying to look as if he wasn't at all bothered by the incident and to give the impression that everyone was making far too much fuss. But he did just manage to mumble, 'Ta missus. Ta very much.'

'Like a cup o' tea, missus?' It was the boys' mother again, emerging from the other boat. 'I've got the pot made, it'll just take a mo to brew.'

'Thank you, yes, that would be nice. And I'm Mrs Walker,' she added, by way of introduction, 'Michael's mother.'

'And I'm Mrs Coleman,' came the reply. 'Me hubby's gone off to find some part for the engine. So we can tie up here for a moment anyway, and wait till he gets back.'

It was unusual for boats to stop before the end of the day, and the two Coleman boys were suddenly unsure what to do with their unexpected break. Vince disappeared into the cabin of the motor boat and pop music was soon heard coming from a portable radio. Kit stood looking rather embarrassed on the path until Mike engaged him in conversation again. He had been wondering about the name of the motor boat, and had tried pronouncing it to himself but couldn't decide whether it was 'Seepheus' or 'Keffy-us' or quite what it might be. So he pointed at the painted panel and asked, 'Where does this boat's name come from?'

'*Cepheus*?' said Kit (who pronounced it 'See-fee-us'). 'Oh, he was some sort of ancient king, an' 'e 'ad a daughter called Andromeda. They're both names of conster-lations though – you know, the stars in the sky. Our boats are from a whole lot that have conster-lation names. There's others called *Orion*, and *Perseus*, and *Leo*, and things like that.'

Mike began to quiz Kit with many of the questions that he had been dying to ask. Kit was happy to answer them, because he was proud of the boats and of his life on the canal. While the two boys talked their mothers were chatting too, over cups of tea.

'My Michael's fascinated by these boats,' Mrs Walker was saying. 'He's always down here watching them. I half-expect him to run away on one, sooner or later.'

'Send him out with us!' said Mrs Coleman. 'If he's that keen. We can certainly make use of him – keep him out of your way for a week or two!' she added, in a tone which suggested she knew all about bored young boys. Mrs Walker was surprised. The boat people were known for keeping themselves to themselves. They didn't have a lot to do with those who lived 'on the bank'.

'I wouldn't want him getting under your feet,' she replied.

'No, I'm bein' serious,' said Kit's mother, earnestly. 'As I say, we can always use extra hands, an' Kit doesn't see many lads his own age, just those as pass by on the other boats. Look at the two of 'em chatting there now, like old pals.' She cast a glance towards the two boys, standing on the bank deep in conversation and both unaware that they were being talked about.

'Kit'd really enjoy having him around, I'm sure. Have a think about it, anyway. We're off to the docks now. But we should be passing here again in four days. Tell us where yer live, and I'll send our Kit round to knock when we get back. If you want your lad to come, just 'ave him ready with his things.'

'I don't know,' said Mike's mother doubtfully. 'I'll have to have a word with his father first. But thanks anyway, it's very kind of you,' she finished cheerfully. 'I'd better get him home now. It's time for his tea and his dad'll be in soon.'

As she spoke another figure appeared on the towpath hurrying towards the boats. The man was in shirtsleeves and overalls tied with a belt, and he wore a black trilby hat. His clothes made him look older than he was, but beneath the brim of his hat he had bright eyes and fine features. Though his skin was deeply tanned through working hard out of doors, he was still a handsome middle-aged man. Mr Coleman carried a rather oily-looking cardboard box, and smiled at his wife as he reached the boat.

'I've got it!' he shouted, first holding the box aloft and then lowering it to show off a shiny metal engine part that lay inside half-wrapped in a tattered piece of rag. Then, as if noticing for the first time that there were strangers present, and that the boats had completely stopped, he looked up, puzzled.

'What's up?' he said.

Mrs Coleman explained about the mishap and how Mrs Walker had tended Vince's injury. Her husband showed more annoyance at the hold-up caused by the springs than concern about his oldest son, and his expression darkened. 'If only I could catch some of them wretched beggars who throw rubbish in the cut, I'd . . . I'd . . .' But he seemed unable to express what he would like to do with the culprits. Instead, Mrs

Coleman spoke up, explaining her suggestion that Mrs Walker's lad should join them on the boats for a week or two. At this Mr Coleman's bright mood returned and he too assured Mrs Walker that they would be glad to have the boy and would take great care of him.

'Well, we'll see,' said Mike's mum. 'Mind you, I don't know how I shall be able to stop him, once he knows you've offered to take him! But I can't promise anything without his father agreeing too.'

'Well, thanks for your help with our Vince, anyway – much obliged I'm sure,' said Mrs Coleman as the family loosed ropes and prepared to continue their journey. 'But have a think about what we've said – we really mean it,' she insisted.

Just in case the invitation should be accepted Mrs Walker carefully explained how to find their house, repeating the street name and their number several times. And as Mr Coleman steered the two boats into the waiting lock his wife mentioned some important things that Mike ought to bring – *if* he should come. Then Mrs Walker called Mike, who eventually tore himself away from helping Kit to close the lock gates behind the boats and hurried down the path after her.

'Oh Mum, you've GOT to let me go!' said Mike for the umpteenth time that evening. After returning home Mike had been told of his mother's conversation with Mrs Coleman. Now the whole prospect of his holidays had suddenly changed and he was really excited. To be actually on the boats, to be on the canal, travelling who-knows-where? Working the locks, being like the boat people he had watched and envied for so long. It was too good to be true; his mum and dad just *had* to let him go. He longed to travel, and live on the water, inside one of those cosy-looking cabins. He had often lain awake at night in his own little bedroom wondering what it would be like to sleep in a bunk on the waterway. Now these vivid thoughts flooded back to him. There'd be a warm stove, he supposed, and little cupboards and drawers for his few things, and the gentle rocking of the boat on the water. It would be a different world. And there would be Kit too. Mike felt they were firm friends already, and couldn't wait to see him again.

'Your dad and I will talk about it later,' his mum said. 'Now there's no more to be said. It's time you were ready for bed anyway.'

In an effort to please his mother Mike dashed upstairs, and with uncharacteristic enthusiasm washed thoroughly, cleaned his teeth and got into his pyjamas. He rushed down the stairs again to say goodnight.

'Have you decided then?' he said, all out of breath.

'We haven't even talked yet, lad! Off to bed now, your dad's still out with his mates. I'll see you in the morning . . . BED!!' she shouted finally, as Mike stood looking blankly at her. Without another word he gave her a quick peck on the cheek, turned and leaped up the stairs two at a time.

Later that evening Mr and Mrs Walker were sitting in front of the television. The News was on, and the Prime Minister Sir Alec Douglas-Home was addressing some journalists about the General Election, but his words went unheard by Mr and Mrs Walker.

'We don't know who these people are, do we?' Mike's dad was saying. 'They might never bring the boy back.'

'Don't be silly, Bob, they're not Gypsies – and that's just Old Wives' Tales anyway. These are perfectly ordinary people; a youngish couple – like us. Our Michael would get a holiday and plenty of fresh air. He's really keen, and even if he didn't like it, at least he would have had a go at it – and we'd hear no more about boats and canals.'

Her husband had to agree that there was little prospect of giving their son any other sort of holiday that year. Things were bad at work; there was no overtime. Mr Walker wasn't earning as much money as he had been used to and he couldn't afford much time off for a holiday. Fortunately Marilyn had been invited to stay at her aunt's, with her cousin Andrea who was one of her best friends. But when Marilyn set off in a couple of days' time it would be hard to explain to Mike that there was nothing planned for him.

'We'd have to arrange everything carefully,' said Mike's father, who liked the idea but didn't want to give in too easily. 'He must have a phone number to keep in touch – perhaps Mrs Aldridge would let us use hers.' The Walkers had no telephone, but occasionally messages would come via their next-door neighbour who had one of the few phones in their street.

'And we must make sure he pays his way. We'll have to give those people some money for his keep.'

'"Those people" are Mr and Mrs Coleman,' his wife reminded him indignantly. 'Of course we must give them some money. I only hope that Michael behaves himself – *if* he goes – and that he doesn't get homesick, and doesn't fall in!' she continued. 'Otherwise I'm quite happy for him to go.'

Without actually expressing their agreement Mr and Mrs Walker seemed to have accepted that Mike was to go on the boats, and the subject was quietly dropped as they settled down on the couch to watch the variety show that had just started. Within a few minutes they were laughing helplessly at a comedian's jokes and all thoughts of canals and holidays were forgotten.

Upstairs meanwhile, Mike could not settle because he was so excited. His head was full of thoughts of a holiday on the canal – his dearest dream, which might be about to come true. He had picked up a book but had been unable to read; the words were just black shapes swimming about in front of his eyes. He had tried listening to his little transistor radio for a while – with the volume turned right down in case his parents should hear. Even that did not succeed in distracting him and eventually he turned it off and put out his light. His mind was restless with thoughts of those wonderful boats, and of adventures up and down the cut. To him the canal was now 'The Cut', just as Kit had called it. If he was going to be a proper boater, he thought, then he would have to learn to use the proper boating words. He realised that he had no idea at all what it would be like actually living on the boats. He could only imagine having a great time with Kit and his family, and the glorious summer days stretching invitingly ahead of him.

His only, but deep and niggling worry, was that his dad would say no. He felt pretty sure that his mum wanted him to go – after all, she had given their address to Kit's mum, and she'd had a sort of smile on her face and laughter in her voice that evening as she scolded him and sent him to bed. He knew his mum very well. But doubts still hovered over his excited thoughts, and they left a weight like a leaden lump in his stomach. Eventually he fell asleep because he was so tired – but how much agony he might have been spared if he had known that downstairs the matter was already settled.

4. A Long Time Waiting

Mike had never known joy like it. He thought back to birthdays and Christmases, and tried to remember any present that had given him as much excitement and pleasure as he felt now, waiting for the boats to return and take him away to adventures unknown. He had packed a bag within ten minutes of his mother telling him at breakfast that he was to be allowed to go. He had hugged her and given her a kiss, but he couldn't thank his dad, who had long since left for work. His mum told him not to be in such a hurry, and she went carefully through all that he had packed into the canvas holdall. But she had to admit that he had been sensible and had thought of most things. The bag contained changes of underwear and socks, tee-shirts and shorts, swimming trunks (he was going to be near water!), pyjamas, some jeans and warm clothing for the cool evenings, and a waterproof for wet days – because he felt sure there were certain to be some. He had even thought to put in a couple of handkerchiefs too, which really impressed his mother.

Mike had also packed a notebook in which he thought he might keep a log of his trip; a bird book in case he should see some unusual ones on the cut; and some special treasures like the Swiss Army knife that his dad had given him last Christmas. His mother still had to add a towel, some toothpaste and soap, and warn him not to forget his toothbrush. In one of his dad's old tobacco tins she also put a pile of pennies and sixpences for the telephone, and a few stamps so that he could send some postcards. Then she produced two half-crowns from her purse for his pocket money, and slipped them into the tin.

'Aw, thanks Mum!' Mike beamed at her.

'Make sure you share it with Kit,' she said. 'He may not get much pocket money himself.'

'I will, I promise,' said Mike. He normally had only a shilling each week, and earned that by doing odd jobs for his mum and dad. Now he had five bob!

Mrs Coleman had said to Mike's mum that he would need a stout belt and some strong shoes or boots, and these were eventually found. The belt was packed, and the boots were put beside his bag where it lay ready in the hall.

That afternoon Mike was back on the canalside at his usual lock. He knew it would be several days before the Colemans returned, but he was hoping to see some pairs going up and down the canal so that he could watch more carefully how the boats and locks were operated. Over the next few days he saw several crews working their craft, and he noted how ropes were tied and cast off, or thrown from boat to boat. He tried to memorise the sequence in which the various sluices were opened and closed to control the water in the locks. He wanted to learn as much as he could before setting off with his new friends. He looked at each boat more carefully, noting where there were fittings such as little bollards, and hooks and rings. He watched the steerers to see how they used their tillers, and he noticed the different ways in which the tarpaulin sheets were fitted over the cargoes, and what sort of loads the boats contained. It seemed mostly to be coal on boats going south, and on those which came from the docks (if the cargo was not concealed by sheets) there was sawn timber, metal tubing, or barrels – which might have contained anything – all going north. Sometimes the boats were empty and rode high in the water.

The weather turned cool and wet the next day and a steady summer downpour continued all afternoon. Even this did not deter Mike, who sheltered beneath the garden walls beside the canal path in his mackintosh and sou'wester. He watched as the rain pelted the surface of the water, destroying the reflections and making bubbles. The boaters kept going through all weathers and Mike was determined that nothing should stop him being like them and braving all conditions. Even the acrid scent of burning coal, wafted on the damp air from the smoking cabin chimneys, spoke to Mike of warm stoves and pots of rich stew simmering gently, ready for a wholesome tea-time meal. Nothing, it seemed, could dampen his enthusiasm for life on the cut.

The only thing that caused Mike any distress in these days of excited waiting was his trip to the barber's. His mum had 'put her foot down' firmly and insisted that he couldn't possibly go away for any length of time with his hair the way it was. 'You'll be looking like the Wild Man of Borneo before long,' she'd said – though Mike had no idea what such a person looked like – and reluctantly he'd taken himself off to Keith's the Gentlemen's Hairdresser. As he sat on the hard seats waiting his turn the electric clippers buzzed, and the harsh strip-lights hummed. The men who were waiting ahead of him all had their faces buried in the pages of the *Daily Express*, or old copies of *Titbits* and the *News of the World*. Mike stared at the yellowing photos around the walls, of young men with hairstyles many years out of date, and listened to the only conversation, which was that of the barber and the client in the chair.

'Been on yer 'olidays yet?' was the barber's unvarying opening line, and Mike heard the men talk of trips to Scarborough or Minehead; of caravan holidays and of Butlins. He smiled inwardly, thinking that these were all very boring compared to the trip he was looking forward to. When his chance came to say that he was going on the canal for his holiday, he felt sure that everyone would be impressed. Then the uncomfortable thought occurred to him that it might seem a very strange idea to other people, and his smile faded. A holiday? On the canal? They'd probably think he was completely daft! So he decided not to say anything about it at all and to steer the conversation towards football instead.

When it was finally his turn in the chair Mike tried to persuade the man to cut off as little as possible, but it did no good. He ended up with his usual short-back-and-sides. And, as if he'd read Mike's thoughts, the barber opened his conversation with, 'Who d'ye want for the Cup then, lad?'

'Had your ears set back, then?' his dad quipped when he came home later. He always used this odd expression to poke fun at his son's severe haircuts. But Mike only scowled and ignored him, feeling that his father was just adding insult to injury. His hair was still fairly long on top, though, and he knew it would soon be flopping into his eyes again, the way he liked it.

On the fourth day Mike could hardly contain himself. No one had any idea exactly what time to expect the Colemans, so his mother suggested that he stay at home instead of going to the canal.

'Kit will come to the house when they arrive, anyway,' she said. 'And the time will pass quicker if you keep yourself busy.'

There were plenty of things to do. There was washing up, and some shopping to be got, and his bedroom needed tidying so it would be clean and neat and ready for him when he returned. Mike knew his mother was right and he did all these things, though in a half-hearted way. But by mid-afternoon, when there was still no sign of Kit and Mike was getting very fidgety, his mother did not try to stop him when he announced that he was going up to the canal to wait.

'You're to come back straight away, though, as soon as they get here,' his mum said firmly. 'I want to have a last word with Mr and Mrs Coleman before you all set off.'

By evening, around halfpast six, when Mike had not returned, his mum was getting a bit anxious. She almost thought he must have gone off without coming to tell her. But his holdall and boots were still sitting on the hall floor under the stairs. So she put on her coat and walked briskly up to the canal where she soon found Mike looking very forlorn, sitting huddled on the balance beam of one of the gates.

'They must have gone past in the night,' he said, almost angrily. He did not even lift up his head, which remained sunk in his hands, but his mother could see the moisture of tears in the corner of his eyes. 'They've gone without me.'

'I expect they've just been held up somewhere,' his mother reassured him gently. 'Come home now and have a cup of tea, love. There's nothing else to be done. Your dad will be in soon and we can talk about what to do.'

Feeling all his energy gone in his disappointment Mike offered no resistance, but followed dejectedly behind his mother. At home he sat in front of the telly, but without any interest in what was on. He didn't like TV much anyway. *Blue Peter* was all right, there were sometimes interesting things on that; and the new science fiction series called *Doctor Who*, that was very exciting. But other kids' programmes, things like *Crackerjack*, he couldn't stand – just a load of silly adults fooling about trying to be funny. In fact the programmes he most liked to see were on ITV, but the Walkers' television set was an old one and it could only get one channel – BBC. To see the adventures of *Stingray* or *Thunderbirds* Mike had to go to his friend Stephen's house, because their TV was more modern. When he got away – *if* he got away – he certainly wouldn't miss the telly. But he didn't feel certain now that he was going anywhere at all.

When Mr Walker came home he had to admit that all they could do was 'wait and see'. He tried to cheer Mike up with some funny stories about what had happened at work, and Marilyn, who was to leave for her auntie's house the next day, offered to let him play whatever music he liked on her record player. Mike wanted to respond to his sister and his dad. He knew they were as disappointed as he was and were only trying to help. But he decided to go to bed instead. As he plodded slowly up the stairs his feet felt as if heavy weights were tied to them. Downstairs his mum and dad simply looked at each other and shrugged their shoulders. There was nothing else they could do to relieve Mike's gloom.

Once again sleep would not come – only this time Mike found it difficult to think happy thoughts. All he could see were empty days ahead with nothing to do, and no one to play with; just his mum saying things like, 'Pop round to your grandma's and see if she wants any shopping.' He didn't want to cry – after all, he was twelve years old – but he certainly felt near to it. To take his mind off things he turned on his transistor radio. The tune that was playing was a popular song that year – 'Messing About on the River'. The music was accompanied by sounds of water slapping against oars or the sides of a boat, and the jolly lyrics were all about having a great time on the water. It wasn't what Mike wanted to hear just at that moment and in a sudden fit of anger he flicked the 'off' switch and stuffed the radio in amongst the clothes in his top drawer, slamming it shut afterwards.

Then, pulling up the covers well over his head, he turned over and drifted into a fitful sleep. He dreamt he was running beside the canal chasing boats which only got further and further away. And there was a barber in his dreams, and a row of men who peered over newspapers and sniggered at him.

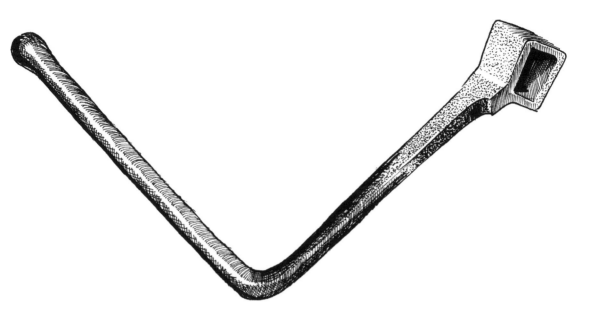

5. Northward Bound

The smell of frying bacon woke Mike the next day. He felt hungry because he'd had no tea the evening before and the aroma of cooking soon lured him out of bed, though it was barely seven o'clock. The thin summer curtains were fluttering in the breeze that blew through his open window and the sun was beating in, lighting up the whole room with a golden glow and warming the lino on the floor. Though Mike awoke with the remains of the sad feelings with which he had gone to bed, and a little bit of an ache in his stomach, the bright new day certainly lifted his spirits.

He pulled on his underpants and a pair of shorts and ran barefoot down to the kitchen where he greeted his mother with a kiss. At breakfast his mum cheered him up with harmless chit-chat – and without mentioning boats or canals or the Colemans at all, and afterwards Auntie Peggy arrived from the bus to collect Marilyn. So there were smiles and laughter and cups of tea and the best biscuits and then Mike and his mother waved madly as aunt and niece set off down the street together.

'Go and put the kettle on, Mike,' said his mother as they went back inside. 'I know we've just had one, but I could do with another cuppa.'

Whilst Mike was lighting the gas and filling the kettle under the tap there was a sharp rap at the front door. Being occupied in the kitchen, Mike could only listen as his mother padded down the hall and reopened the door, which had just been closed on his departing sister. Perhaps Marilyn had forgotten something, he thought. Then his mother called him.

'Michael! Come and see who it is.'

The kettle was thrown roughly onto the lighted hob and Mike's heart raced as he skidded out of the kitchen and half-ran, half-slid down the polished floor of the hall. At the front door he could see Kit's unmistakable red-gold hair, which glowed as though he were full of sunshine.

'Hurray!!' shouted Mike to the whole world; and then to Kit, 'I'm ready – just let me get my boots on,' and he disappeared back down the hall. Meanwhile Kit was apologising and explaining to Mrs Walker how they had been delayed on the previous afternoon.

'Me mum says, very sorry we're late, but there was an 'old-up, 'bout three miles back down the cut. A bridge was bein' repaired. It was a 'mergency – a lorry 'it it – so we 'ad to tie up there for the night. Made good time this mornin' though, and Mum and Dad and our Vince are workin' the boats up the locks now. I 'spect we'll catch 'em near the top.'

Mike reappeared with his bag. His mother hurried back to the kitchen to turn off the gas under the kettle before grabbing her handbag and locking the door behind her. Then she followed the two lads who had already begun to walk briskly up the street.

'I thought you'd gone past and forgotten about me,' complained Mike.

'No, never!' said Kit. 'Sorry we're late, but you never know what things are gonna 'appen on the cut, and there wasn't any way we could tell yer we was stuck.'

'It don't matter now,' Mike replied. He seemed to have forgotten all the woes of yesterday already. He was eager to ask lots of questions, like 'where will I be sleeping?' and 'how far shall we be going?' and 'what's your dad like?' But it didn't seem to be the right moment for such a quiz, so he followed dutifully where Kit led, and soon they were on the grassy path beside the water. Looking north they could see that the boats had gone through the lock where Mike usually played and were nearly ready to leave the lock above.

'Come on,' said Kit, 'me dad will be moaning if we keep 'em waiting.'

'My mum isn't here yet,' Mike said. But as he spoke Mrs Walker appeared from the narrow alley and soon caught them up; indeed she ignored the two boys and set off ahead and almost ran up the slope of the next lock, calling to Mrs Coleman as she went.

'Thanks ever so,' she said, reaching the boats and catching her breath. Mrs Coleman was at the tiller of *Andromeda* and simply replied, 'We'll look after him, don't you worry. You'll get him back in one piece – an' he'll look fitter and healthier than you've ever seen him before!'

'You must take this,' said Mrs Walker, proffering a brown ten-shilling note, which she had drawn out of her bag. 'He's a hungry lad, and I don't want you to be out of pocket.'

'Well, I'm sure he'll earn his keep while he's with us, Mrs Walker. But I'm very much obliged to you,' and she accepted the banknote with a smile and slipped it into the pocket of her apron.

'He's got pocket money and coins for the phone as well,' said Mike's mother. 'Will you make sure he gives us a call every now and then?'

'Don't be worrying,' said Mrs Coleman. 'I'll make sure he don't forget his folks – nor anything else he should be doing neither.'

'Thanks,' said Mrs Walker, then she chuckled, 'Now I'll be off – I'm sure our Michael wouldn't appreciate any sentimental farewells!' Mrs Coleman smiled and waved Mrs Walker goodbye. 'Don't worry!' she shouted one more time as Mike's mother briefly grabbed her son, gave him a sloppy kiss on the cheek, said, 'Behave yourself!' and then set off back down the path without turning or waving, until she rounded the corner into the alley and disappeared.

'Give us yer bag, Mike!' shouted Mr Coleman cheerily from where he stood at the tiller of the motor boat. 'I'll put it away safely for yer, in the cabin.'

Mike passed his holdall to Kit's dad and then his heart leapt for sheer joy as he went to step aboard the motor boat – the first time he had actually left the bank of the canal to join one of the craft.

'Hold on there just a minute, young man!' said Mr Coleman. 'There's a lock or two to get through yet. You run on ahead with our Kit and give him a hand, there's a good chap!'

Mike felt a brief pang of disappointment, because his first waterborne experience had ended almost before it had begun. But nothing could dampen his excitement now, and he dutifully leaped ashore, shouting 'Okay!' to the boats' captain. Then he ran up the path to join Kit who was already opening the gates of the lock above.

His adventure had finally begun, and he was more than happy just to be part of this family team. He was determined to be content doing any job he was given and he felt, deep in his heart, that there would be lots and lots of new and different experiences to share with his new friends and the winding waters of the cut. He was going to make the very most of every moment.

As he ran Mike heard the engine revs increase, and turned to see a fine column of blue diesel smoke puffing vigorously into the morning air as Mr Coleman brought the pair out from the lock below and carefully lined them up to enter the next one. And there was Vince, his shining hair neatly combed into a quiff above his forehead, chewing gum whilst he stood at the stern of the companion boat. He had little to do until the lock was reached, because his father steered both the tied boats together.

Then Mike got a surprise. As he glanced back he saw a red-headed little girl peeping out of the cabin in front of Vince. She cast a quick glance at Mike and then clambered up onto the cabin roof where there was a large enamelled bowl full of peas. She sat down, crossing her legs, and made herself comfortable in the sunshine. She began to shell the peas, carefully placing them in a saucepan and the empty pods back in the bowl. It seemed that Kit and Vince had a little sister. Mike had not had a chance to ask Kit much about his family and now he wondered whether there were any more of them, hidden away down in the little cabins. As the girl applied herself to her task she didn't seem to be bothered by the movement of the boats and the flurry of activity that was going on around her at the lock, where Mike was now ready to help Kit with the gates.

'That's Susannah,' said Kit, who had noticed the look of surprise on Mike's face. 'She's ten, but she's all right. We 'ave some fun, our Sis and me. Now come on, and I'll show yer how to use this!'

Kit brandished his metal handle in the air, then instructed Mike how it was used to open and close the sluices which controlled the water, and how important it was to make sure that the water flow did not swamp the boats in the lock.

'This is a windlass,' he explained, 'though we calls it an "iron". We'll find you one of your own soon, but you can use mine for now. The important thing is that you NEVER goes off and leave it lyin' around on the lock, and you NEVER drops it in the cut. When you're not usin' it you can keep it 'ere.' And he showed Mike how the V-shape of the handle tucked neatly into his belt behind his back.

'These are called paddles,' said Kit, indicating the gear on the gates by patting the black-painted metalwork with his hand. 'They're sort of trap-doors which let the water in and out.' Mike readily understood Kit's instructions and explanations because he had spent so much time carefully watching how all the boaters used their windlasses. What he wasn't prepared for was the huge effort required to wind the handle on the iron shaft, and he soon found that the job was much harder than the boaters made it appear. Mike struggled to turn the large handle on the stiff and worn spindle, and it took him a moment or two to get the paddle up. But as he fought with the reluctant machinery he could hear the satisfying roar of water pouring into the lock, and from far below a refreshing cool breeze, laden with fine spray, drifted up and dampened his face. The moist draught had a distinct and pleasant fragrance – rather like a garden after a shower of rain, when the scent of grass and flowers is so strong and sweet.

Together Mike and Kit worked ahead of the boats, preparing each lock, whilst Vince and his mum worked the gates and the ropes which held the boats in check. In this way they soon reached the edge of the town. At the last lock they met another pair coming down, in the opposite direction. This meant that the lock was emptied and left ready for them and the two boys were able to take a rest. They waved cheerfully to the steerer as the other boats passed and Kit shouted, 'How d'ye do, Mr Jackson?' The old man lifted a hand in greeting and replied ''Ow do, young Kit?'

'And this is Mike!' Kit said, jabbing a finger in the direction of his friend.

''Ow do, young Mike?' came the reply, accompanied by another brief wave of the hand.

Mike began to realise that very little changed on the cut, and that the life and manners of the boaters changed little too. This old-fashioned greeting seemed to be used by everyone on the boats, and Mike felt that before long he would find himself using it too.

'You know him, then?' he said to Kit.

'We knows everyone on the boats, nearly,' Kit said. 'They all live and work on the cut, so we sees 'em often enough. But we don't get much chance to talk, 'cept when we're tied up at the end of the day, or if we're waitin' to load and unload.'

As Mr Jackson's pair passed the Colemans' boats, Kit's mum shared bits of news with those on board. They all spoke very quickly and all at once, and shouted to be heard as the boats drifted further apart. They might not have much time to talk, thought Mike, but they make the most of what little there is!

Beyond the lock there stretched ahead of them a level of uninterrupted water. When the lock was full and the gates opened Mr Coleman shouted, 'All aboard!' and Kit scrambled onto the side of his dad's boat, holding out his hand to Mike and pulling him up onto the narrow gunwale. As the boats left the lock Mike could see that the ropes which had joined the pair had been loosed off and now the second boat was being pulled behind the first on the end of a very long line. Vince, at the tiller of the second boat, was barely visible in the distance as the two craft gradually drew apart and the line tautened.

The canal, looking like a silvery ribbon, led out of the fringes of the town and into the wide-open countryside. Everything appeared different from the water. There were unfamiliar farm cottages and spinnies, remote fields and distant woods; a horse or two here, some cattle there, and occasionally a track led up to the waterway and crossed it on a tiny brick bridge. There were no roads in sight, and Mike hardly recognised the scenery round about him. It was a bit like travelling on the train, when you passed by people's back windows and gardens and places which are normally hidden from view. Now he was on the canal, which looked into the back yard of the countryside, and it was mostly quiet and still – unlike the scene on the busy roads, with their cafes and pubs, and bus stops and cyclists, and rushing lorries and cars.

6. A Home on the Water

'Let's get yer things sorted out,' said Kit, indicating that Mike should follow him below. He nimbly edged his way to the rear of the cabin and, darting past his father who stood in the cabin doorway, disappeared backwards into the tiny space. Mike followed him more cautiously and as he turned round to climb down into the cabin he heard Kit shout, 'Careful on the step!'

In a moment Mike was inside the cabin of a narrow boat for the very first time. He was eager to inspect his new quarters; this neat and compact living arrangement which was to be his home for the next . . . well, he didn't know how long it might be – possibly a couple of weeks. It seemed a little dark at first, the light coming mainly through the open doorway where he had entered. There was also a single porthole on the right-hand side of the boat and in the ceiling a thick glass skylight about the size of a tea plate.

'You're in 'ere with me an' our Vince,' Kit explained, raising his voice to be heard over the sound of the engine that throbbed steadily in the next compartment. 'Mum and Dad and our Susannah are on the butty.'

Mike looked at him blankly.

'You've got a lotta new things to learn, 'aven't you?' smiled Kit. 'The "butty" is what we call the other boat, *Andromeda* – it's the one wivvout an engine; and this one is the "motor". All the pairs of boats 'ave a motor an' a butty. Now, there's not much space,' he went on, 'but if you're careful and tidy, everything'll go in and we won't be too cramped.'

Then Kit gave Mike a little guided tour of the cabin's interior. To the left-hand side of the step down which they had just climbed there was a small black cast-iron range, and Mike noticed that the step itself was actually the front edge of a stout wooden box that contained coal for the fire. The range wasn't alight because, as Kit explained, all the cooking was done on a similar stove in the butty boat. This one was only lit when the weather was cold, and then the large brown enamelled kettle, which stood on the polished top, could be used all day to make refreshing cups of tea. A broad pipe from the top of the stove went out through the cabin roof – to the chimney with the brass rings that Mike had noted before.

Beyond the range were cupboards and drawers from floor to ceiling. Kit opened one cupboard, whose door folded down level to form a little table. Inside on the shelves were cups and plates, some tinned foods and jars of jam and pickles, and a few books and magazines. The largest cupboard of all also folded down, and joined onto a bench on the right-hand side to form a wide bed across the width of the boat at the back of the cabin. Inside this cupboard was a rolled-up mattress and all the bedding, ready to be set out. Along the right-hand side of the cabin there was just a narrow bed which could be used during the day as a seat, and from which one could work or eat at the little table. Mike noticed that much of the woodwork in the cabin was brightly painted with clusters of colourful roses and other designs; and on the door of the table cupboard he saw a small scene of a castle beside a river, with flags flying from the turrets.

'All the boats 'ave 'em,' explained Kit. 'They're tradish'nal. People've been paintin' 'em for as long as anyone can remember. Sometimes you see boats with roses an' castles painted on the outside as well, but ours are just plain blue an' yellow.

'You can sleep 'ere,' he continued, indicating the side-bed on the right. And lifting a lid beneath the bedding of the narrow bunk Kit revealed some empty space below. 'You can pack yer things in here, Mike,' he said. 'And put your towel with the others on that rail over the stove.' Soon the few items which had filled Mike's sparsely-packed bag were stowed neatly away. His tobacco tin which contained his pocket money, phone coins and Mrs Aldridge's telephone number written on a scrap of paper, went into the table cupboard with the books and plates and tins. His Swiss Army knife he put in a little drawer beneath, which contained cutlery and a few tools. Mike would have preferred to carry it with him, in a pocket, but he was afraid that he might be careless and lose it in the cut.

The two boys sat for a while on the side-bed, talking. 'We should get to a really good stopping-place tonight,' said Kit. 'You'll like it. It's one of me mum and dad's favourite pubs, right out in the country, so there's usually only us boaters there. But it's busy 'cause there's a wharf there an' a shop, and other boats tie up for the night. We can play outside an' 'ave a laugh.'

Michael's head was going round and round with sheer joy and excitement; he was actually on a narrow boat; he had his own bed in this fantastically cosy cabin, and now Kit was promising all sorts of exciting things to come. But at the back of Mike's mind there was still one niggling question, and now he plucked up courage to ask it.

'Kit,' he said cautiously, and his friend looked at him in silent expectation. 'Well, I was just going to ask . . .' Mike still hesitated, looking a bit embarrassed. 'I was only going to ask – where do you go to the lavatory?'

Kit's blank expression changed instantly. His face rounded into a broad grin and he started to chuckle. Then he began to rock back and forth, and his laughter grew louder and wilder. Soon Mike began to giggle too. Within moments the two of them were lying on their backs laughing uncontrollably, the tears running down their cheeks.

It took a while for them to calm down and even then it was difficult for Kit to speak. Every time he tried to say something he just started giggling again.

'You go . . . you go . . . in the engine 'ole,' he managed to say at last, 'for serious stuff. There's an Elsan in there.' He jerked a thumb towards the wall at the end of the cabin, indicating the engine compartment. Mike had used Elsan lavatories before, on campsites with his mum and dad. They were little better than buckets filled with special chemicals to stop them smelling, and he wasn't very keen on them. It was strange that he'd never wondered about this important matter before in all his thoughts about life on the boats. But if you were always on the move it was obvious that there was no easy solution.

'And you can wee in the bushes on the towpath,' added Kit, 'if you're doing the locks, or if you can jump off the boats.'

Mike had often been with his dad on walks in the countryside, and knew it was quite usual to pee in the hedgerows, away from the footpaths. He felt happier about that idea. Well, he was certainly learning lots of things very quickly about boating life!

Kit's giggles subsided, and at last he recovered himself. 'Let's go out again,' he suggested. It was rather stuffy in the cabin and the engine noise meant that they had to raise their voices to be heard. Mike took another affectionate look around his new home then followed Kit up the steps.

'What's been tickling you two?' asked Mr Coleman, as the boys climbed up onto the cabin roof and sat down, facing him.

'Oh, nuffin' much,' said his son. 'I was only explaining to Mike about our luxury bathroom with all mod cons,' and he began to chuckle again.

'I 'spect you'll find ev'rythin' a bit strange at first,' Mr Coleman said to Mike. 'We're used to this life, but it must seem very different to you.'

'I'll get used to it,' said Mike cheerfully. 'It's a bit like camping really – only much better of course, and lots more fun,' he added quickly, hoping he hadn't offended anyone.

'You like our boats then?' said Kit's dad, proudly.

'They're smashing,' said Mike, who secretly wondered why anyone would want to live in a house and stay in the same place all the time, when on the boats the scenery changed minute by minute and – best of all – you were out in the fresh air. He also reflected to himself that the two boat cabins put together were probably smaller than his own bedroom at home – the smallest in his house. Yet they provided for all the needs of this family.

By now the canal had entered a deep, tree-lined cutting where the banks rose up steeply on either side. Tall chestnuts and beeches leaned towards each other over the water, their lofty tops touching in the middle. The light had a greenish tinge as it came in hazy shafts through the high boughs. The surface of the cut only sparkled here and there as the sunlight penetrated the leafy canopy, and the air felt cool in the shadier places. As the leaves fluttered in the breeze, so the dappled light flickered and danced playfully on the cabin roofs and the tarpaulin covers of the boats, chasing the shadows round and round as if in a game. The water in turn reflected rippling sunbeams onto the trunks of the trees, which appeared to sway as the light played on them.

'We're going round the summit pound,' said Mr Coleman to Mike. 'Each stretch of water between the locks is called a pound, whether it's a short one or a long un like this. We've been climbing up the locks so far, and this is the highest level, the summit. After this pound we'll start going down again. But there's only seven more locks to do today.'

In a little while the cutting began to broaden out, and soon open fields were visible again on one side of the canal. On the other, in the distance, Mike could hear the sound of a railway train roaring past on the main line hidden from the cut by the trees. Not for the first time did he feel he had entered a secret world, a slower, gentler way of life that existed unnoticed by the other, busier world on the land.

'Come an' 'ave a look at the butty,' Kit said suddenly, pulling Mike's sleeve as he slid down onto the gunwale of the boat.

'Don't go annoying your mother and Vince, Kit,' said Mr Coleman. 'And the locks will be coming up soon.'

'I know Dad,' Kit replied. 'It'll only be a quick visit.'

Mike stared back down the canal at the distant *Andromeda* as she followed in the wake of *Cepheus*, and found himself wondering how Kit was going to get him to the butty boat. A wild thought entered his head and he pictured himself doing a tightrope act down the long, taut line which linked the two craft, or swinging along beneath it, as if on an obstacle course.

'How are we . . . ?' Mike began.

'Jus' follow me, quick!' Kit said, looking steadfastly ahead. The boat had almost reached one of the narrow brick bridges that carry minor roads and cart tracks across the canal. Because the bridges were so small the wide waters of the cut narrowed to pass through the archway and the path at the side of the canal also swung inwards and tucked itself into the constricted space. The dusty track was therefore only inches away from the side of the boat as it entered the bridge arch.

'Jump!' shouted Kit, and together the two boys sprang onto the path beneath the bridge. The ground seemed suddenly very hard and solid to Mike after the gentle movement of the boat beneath his feet. The motor passed on up the cut and the butty boat drew nearer, following on its long line.

'Mind yer 'ead on the bridge when we gets on,' warned Kit, turning to Mike for a moment. Then as the stern of the butty came alongside where they waited he jumped over the gunwale and Mike followed him.

'Clear off, Kit!' his brother shouted, as the boys leapt aboard. 'There ain't no room! What d'yer wanna come on 'ere for?' And it was true that it was a tight squeeze with the three of them standing in the hatches.

'Okay, okay!' said his brother. 'I'm jus' doin' a quick guided tour for Mike. We'll get off at the next bridge'ole to do the locks.'

To the boat people, who mainly saw bridges from the water, the only important part of any bridge was the archway or 'hole' through which they passed. Therefore they rarely referred to 'bridges' but only to 'bridge-holes'.

Inside the butty cabin Mike noticed all the same fixtures and fittings – the cupboards and table and bunks – that he had seen in the motor. The cabins were practically identical, though this one was a bit roomier. The stove was alight and the cabin was very warm. Susannah was resting on the cross-bed, which was folded down at the back of the cabin. Mrs Coleman was busy cooking and the kettle was simmering, ready for cups of tea that would be passed around at the next locks.

'Hullo Mike,' she said. 'Come to see how the other 'arf live?'

Mike didn't really get her little joke, but he smiled, and sat on the side-bed for a moment or two as Mrs Coleman invited him to do. Around him were more decorative things than he'd seen on the motor. Many delicate-looking plates with frilly edges hung in overlapping rows. There were some family photos, lots of lacy fringes, and bits and pieces of brass which were so brightly polished that everything was reflected in their glass-like surfaces.

'I 'ope you likes hotpot,' said Kit's mum, as she diced carrots at the table.

'Mmm, I love it!' Mike replied, licking his lips hungrily. 'It's one of my favourites.' He was being quite truthful as he spoke, because his own mother was a good cook and of all the things she made he liked best her Sunday roasts and her stews and soups and hotpots. She also made lovely puddings and cakes. In fact Mike enjoyed eating most things, but he was lucky because his mother had time to cook varied and wholesome meals, and he'd always been taught to eat what was put in front of him.

'And there's rice pud for afters,' continued Mrs Coleman.

'Yummy!' said Mike, who felt once again that he was really going to enjoy life aboard the boats.

'Come on then,' said Kit, leaping up from the seat. 'Can't sit 'ere all day. There's work to be done!'

'Listen to him!' said his mother. 'It's usually *me* that has to say that to *him*!'

The boys climbed out of the cabin, and Mike could see another bridge-hole approaching. Then Kit suddenly remembered something.

'Oh no! I've left me iron on the motor,' he cried. 'Can I lend yours, Vince?'

'DON'T lose it!' said his brother, with a threatening look. Kit grabbed the essential windlass from the cabin roof, then hopped over the side shouting, 'Geronimo!!' Mike followed him as Vince steered the butty close to the path beneath the bridge.

The two boys sprinted along the grassy bank towards the lock which was only a couple of hundred yards away, its black and white painted woodwork standing out clearly amidst the green of the countryside and the broad blue sky. As he ran in the warm afternoon air, startled birds flew from the water-margins squawking in protest at his passing, and Mike suddenly felt a tremendous exhilaration in this new-found freedom. Though he had not stopped to think about it properly, he was already some distance from his home. He was quickly becoming a part of this very different way of life. He was deliriously happy, and so far had not spared a single thought for the familiar things he'd left behind. Days and days of his summer holiday still lay before him, and he was completely absorbed by the excitement and novelty of life on 'The Cut.'

7. At the Wharf Inn

Voices in cheerful conversation could be heard through the open windows of the little pub. Occasionally the voices erupted into roars of laughter. The pub was a plain and simple building, with a slate roof and a small painted sign over the door proclaiming it to be 'The Wharf Inn'. Besides the Colemans, two more pairs of boats had moored near the loading place which gave the pub its name, and their crews were now catching up on all the news of the cut over a glass of beer. The women had gathered in a snug corner of the small, low-ceilinged room and the men were mainly standing about the bar which was wreathed in the sweet smoke of pipe tobacco and hand-rolled cigarettes. The uneven red-tiled floor was neatly swept and a few ancient tables and chairs was the only furniture. It was nearly nine o'clock and outside Mike and Kit were sitting on some empty barrels with Susannah. They had each been bought a bottle of Vimto and packets of crisps. The pub was set back from the water's edge and in front of them a patch of rough grass led down to the canalside where *Cepheus* and *Andromeda* lay tied up for the night. They had reached their mooring by about seven o'clock after working quickly through the last locks. These had all been set in their favour by a pair of boats passing in the opposite direction. It had been a perfect end to the day, Kit's dad had said.

Before their evening meal of hotpot and rice pudding the boys had been set to polish all the brass, especially the rings on the two cabin chimneys, and with a mop each they had also washed down the sides of the cabins so that both craft looked neat and clean. They had tried to outdo each other in the polishing and mopping and Mrs Coleman had remarked that they would wear the boats away to nothing with their frantic efforts. The last task had been to take the water cans to the tap at the wharf for filling. These large cans each contained about two gallons – the only supply of fresh water for the boats. There were two cans on the butty and one on the motor and they were normally kept in front of the chimney on the cabin roof. Unlike water cans that are used for camping these were beautifully painted. Each of them was decorated with more groups of roses like those in the cabin paintings, and on a yellow band around the middle of each can was painted the boat's name and the family name 'Coleman' in curly red letters. The cans were heavy when full and the boys struggled a little with a can each. They made two trips, and carried the third one between them. Once in position on the cabin tops the mops were laid in front of the cans – one on each boat – their shafts propped up against the can handles. Like most other things that he had seen Mike realised that even the position of the water cans and mops was traditional, the same on every boat and unchanged in many, many years.

When they had all gathered together on the butty at tea-time Mr and Mrs Coleman had their first chance to talk to Mike and ask him questions about himself and his family. He told them that his dad worked in an engineering factory, but that the firm was short of work at the moment. 'That's why we couldn't have a holiday all together this year,' he explained. 'But Dad's not bothered, he's got his hobbies. He grows lots of things on his allotment and he loves going to the Speedway,' Mike explained, 'where they race motorbikes. That's what he likes doing best. He's happy as long as he can still do that.' Vince's face lit up at Mike's words.

'You'd enjoy the Speedway, wouldn't you, Vince?' Mrs Coleman said, looking at her son. Vince nodded. 'It'd be smashing. Trouble is,' he said, grumpily, 'we never stop anywhere long enough for me to go.'

Mike continued, telling them that his mum was mostly at home, but that she was also a dinner lady, doing a few hours each day at the school. At the moment she was also doing millinery classes in the evening, learning to make fashionable hats. Mrs Coleman asked him whether he had brothers and sisters and everyone was interested to hear about Marilyn.

'I've got a sister too,' said Susannah, taking Mike by surprise once again – he thought he had seen all the Colemans by now and wondered where this other girl might be. Mr Coleman provided the answer. 'Joyce works with her auntie and uncle, Mike.'

'Yes, Daisy and Alf haven't got any children of their own,' Mrs Coleman explained, 'and we wus getting a bit crowded on our boats. Joyce is eighteen now, and so she lives with them an' 'elps with their boats instead. It often 'appens in boating families that some of the children go and work with relatives.'

'We still see her now an' again,' said Susannah, 'because we're always passing their boats as we go up and

down.'

'And sometimes we find ourselves tying up together in the same stop,' said Kit, 'then we all 'as a good gossip and catch up with the news.'

'Oh yes,' said Mr Coleman, confidently, 'I expect you'll see our Joyce before very long.'

'How old are you, Mike?' asked Susannah.

'I'm twelve,' he replied, 'but I shall be thirteen very soon,' he added proudly.

'You're nearly as old as our Kit then,' said Mr Coleman. 'He's thirteen already, and won't be fourteen for a few months yet.'

'And Vince is seventeen,' said Mrs Coleman, as if she knew that Mike was about to ask. 'But I don't know how much longer he'll be with us – you're not that keen to stay on the boats, are you, Vince?' she remarked to the older boy. 'Still, he's not going to leave us just yet, anyhow.'

Vince hadn't taken a lot of interest in the conversation, and remained silent now. He merely nodded his head in a grudging sort of way. He had been friendly to Mike, but somehow he always gave the impression that he would rather be somewhere else. Vince really longed for the company of young people of his own age, and being a lad from the boats wasn't particularly glamorous when it came to making friends. He wasn't exactly ashamed of his way of life, he was proud of it really. But other people – people off the bank – didn't understand it, and that made things difficult for a self-conscious teenager who wanted to be 'with it'.

Mrs Coleman's cooking had been received with enthusiasm and plates had been emptied in a matter of moments and mopped clean with hunks of bread.

'It's the fresh air and the 'ard work, Mike,' she had said. 'You'll always have a good appetite when you're working on the boats!'

Mike was pleased by her words, and felt a surge of pride. Till now he had thought of himself as having a holiday. But Mrs Coleman was right, he was actually at *work*, just like Kit and Vince and all of them – even Susannah, because she helped with the cooking and even steered the butty sometimes. He was twelve years old – well, nearly thirteen – and working as part of a proper boating family, part of the team. Each had their own jobs to do, and together they kept the boats moving. 'That's the important thing in this lark,' Mr Coleman had said to Mike. 'Keep the boats movin'. If they're standin' idle, then they're not earnin' us any money!'

At eight o'clock the sky was still bright with summer sunshine and they were enjoying a rest. After their tea Mrs Coleman and Vince had gone to the little shop which was really just a room on one side of the pub, and was run by the landlord's sister. Unlike most town shops this one was open at all hours because it was especially for the boaters, who had very little time to go shopping. It was filled from floor to ceiling with tins and boxes and trays of this and that: groceries, haberdashery, paraffin for cabin lamps, ironmongery, soap and shampoo, and some basic medicines. Everything was piled anyhow – not like the neat displays of the shops in the high street. But the shopkeeper knew just where to find all the things that her customers asked for, and she had a good supply of fresh bread, and vegetables, eggs and milk, which came from the local farms and market gardens.

When Kit's mum and brother had returned and the provisions were stowed away, everyone had got ready to go to the pub. Mike had changed his shorts for jeans and put on a pair of plimsolls. He was glad to take off his heavy boots after running around in them all day. Kit had simply put on a sweater over his shirt. Vince, in his smart leather jacket and 'drainpipe' jeans, went into the pub with his mum and dad. In this remote part of the countryside no one was particularly bothered about a young lad being in the bar. He sometimes had lemonade or shandy, but Kit knew that his dad usually bought his brother beer and that he drank with the men.

For a while Kit, Mike and Susannah had played football on the grass outside with some children from the other boats. Susannah had proved herself one of the best both at tackling and scoring, rather to the annoyance of her brother who wanted to show off to Mike. Later they'd played hide and seek, but again Susannah had outwitted the two boys and they'd given up looking after she managed to conceal herself successfully in a tiny space between two tumble-down sheds, with a sack drawn over her head. The other children had got bored and gone off to play elsewhere whilst Kit and Mike searched and searched calling, 'Susie, where are you?' Afterwards the three of them had rested on the barrels and talked for a while about what had happened that day and where they were going tomorrow. Then the conversation had dried up and for a few moments they sat in silence.

'That's enough now. Go away, you fat old thing!' Susannah spoke to the large retriever dog, which had appeared the moment that Mr Coleman brought crisps out to the children. They had fed her with one or two of the salty chips, but she was still looking at them with a hopeful expression and was dribbling onto the brick pavement where the barrels stood. The dog was obviously not intending to move, but eventually realised that the packets were empty, and she waddled slowly away, back through the door of the pub.

After Susannah had broken the silence Mike started up the conversation again. 'Don't you ever go to school?' he said to Kit. His friend laughed.

'We're s'posed to,' he replied, smiling. 'But it's not easy when you're always movin' about! Vince and me used to go to a school on the bank, down in London. We only went there now and then, when the boats were tied up there. But it was all right. They 'ad games fields and we could play with other kids, as well as 'aving some lessons. Susannah went there a few times as well, but it's closed now. They're talking about getting us off the boats. They want us to go to a school in Brummagem; we'd have to live there as well, and I don't really wanna do that.'

'Nor me,' said Susannah. 'Our mum teaches us most things, anyway. She went to school a bit once. She can read and write. Most of the old people can't read nor write at all.'

'Dad can only read and write a little bit,' said Kit. 'He was born on the boats an' his family have always been boaters. Dad didn't get much time at school when he was a youngster – but of course he knows ev'ryfing there is to know about boating. But our mum's from a family off the bank.'

Kit explained how his mum had started working on the boats during the Second World War. She was a very young woman then, he told Mike. The canal company was short of crews because lots of the men had gone off to fight, so they had recruited girls as trainees to run the boats. She had met their dad on the cut, and they had married at the end of the war.

'Mum tried to teach Dad to read and write, and sometimes she gives us lessons. Susannah's the best at readin', but none of us is good at writin'!'

Mike thought of the journey he made to school, five days a week, and the hours he had spent looking out of the classroom window wishing he were somewhere else. He had to admit to himself that, on the whole, he liked school. But he remembered all the fuss there had been one day when he'd decided not to go, and had spent the time wandering the streets and playing in the park instead. He had been severely punished at home and reprimanded by the headmistress at the school – and that was for just one day he had been missing! Yet no one, it seemed, was bothered whether the children on the boats went to school or not.

'I've got to go to a new school when I get back,' said Mike, realising that this was the first time he had thought of home and what was in store for him next term. But sitting in the fresh air and the fading evening light, with the merry sounds of the pub behind him and the tranquil countryside all about him, home and school all seemed rather remote, and unreal, and unimportant.

Trying to focus on this idea, he continued, 'I don't mind it, really. All my mates are going to the same school. It'll be better there anyway, because you're with older kids, instead of all the tinies.' Then he noticed Susannah giving him a funny look.

'Not like you,' he added, hoping he hadn't offended her. 'I mean, the infants and lower juniors. You're like our age group anyway, and you're much better at things than a lot of the younger kids I know.'

Mrs Coleman came out of the pub and approached the children. 'Come on, Susannah! Back to the boats with me. It'll soon be time for you to get ready for bed.'

Mike half-expected the young girl to protest at being taken away, but Susannah dutifully followed her mother, saying, 'See ya!' to the two boys, and skipping happily away down to the waterside. The life of the boating people was very demanding and children were usually taught what to do and what not to do for their own safety – there were many dangers on the canal, which could easily trap the foolish or careless. So the Coleman children were quite used to obeying their parents, and rarely made a fuss as other children often do.

'Me dad'll come out and send us 'ome in a minute,' Kit said. 'But I'm tired anyway.'

'Me too,' admitted Mike. He was enjoying himself thoroughly, but he couldn't disguise the fact that it had been a tiring day and he was looking forward to climbing into his little bunk aboard *Cepheus*.

'Stars are comin' out,' said Kit, gazing up at the sky which was beginning to turn a deep blue, though the fleeting sunlight still lit up the distant horizon in the west. 'I likes looking at all the different conster-lations, an' the planets,' he continued, 'specially in the autumn an' winter when the sky's really black and all the stars stand out like di'monds. We get a long way out of the towns sometimes, like tonight, away from all the street lights. And when it gets dark, it's *really* dark.'

'I can see several faint ones already,' said Mike.

'That one right over'ead is Vega,' said Kit, pointing. He began to sweep his arm in a wide arc, saying, 'An' there's some of the stars from Cygnus the Swan, and some from Cassiopeia. And in between, though you can't really see 'em yet, is Cepheus – the one that our motor is named after.' He dropped his arm, which was beginning to ache, and looked at Mike who was still gazing into the heavens.

'What's that one on the horizon over there, that really bright one?' asked Mike.

'Ah! Tha's the Evenin' Star, only it's not a star really. It's Venus, the planet,' replied Kit.

'You know a lot about astronomy,' said Mike, who was impressed.

'Me mum taught me a lot of the names. You see, us boaters are up at all hours of the night sometimes, especially in winter when it gets dark early and the dawn is very late. We get to know the night sky very well. I likes the winter conster'lations best. I likes Orion with his belt and sword, and I like the big dog, Canis Major. He has a star called Sirius, which twinkles all different colours. It looks really beautiful, an' it's my favourite star of all. If I ever get a boat of my own,' he went on wistfully, 'it's gonna be called *Sirius*.'

This set off another train of questions in Mike's mind, about what Kit wanted to do when he grew up. But as he started to speak again a loud voice interrupted him.

'Hey, you boys! Get off back to the boats now, there's good lads.' It was Mr Coleman, who had just stuck his head round the door of the pub. Mike and Kit passed him their empty bottles, said 'Goodnight,' and then set off down the grassy slope.

'G'night lads, sleep tight!' Mr Coleman called after them, before disappearing back into the bar, which was still filled with the boaters and their friendly chatter.

As they walked slowly back to the canalside Kit looked up once more and pointed to a W-shaped group of stars. 'Those are the ones called Cassiopeia. It's funny,' he said, 'in the old stories Cassiopeia was the wife of Cepheus, and I've wondered sometimes why our butty is called Andromeda, who was his daughter, and not Cassiopeia, his missus. It don't really matter I s'pose, though there is a boat called *Cassiopeia*. I 'spect it's just the way the Company named the boats and paired them up.'

Their boats lay peacefully on the water. With the relentless chugging of the engine silenced, all was calm and hushed. The toil and hurry of the day's work was over. In the fading light all colour had fled from the waterside; only grey shadows remained. Around them a few glints of yellow light shone dimly from the open hatches or portholes of neighbouring boats. The surface of the water was still, like glass, reflecting the pale glow of the western horizon. From far in the distance, back down the cut in the direction from which they had travelled, came the sound of running water in the last lock, clear and musical on the still night air. The only other occasional, melancholy sound was that of a nocturnal bird, a thin and lonely cry in the darkness. The two boys climbed carefully aboard *Cepheus* and the craft gently yielded to their weight, swaying slightly on its mooring. Inside Kit flicked a little brass switch and the cabin was instantly flooded with bright electric light.

'Some o' the old boats still has oil lamps,' said Kit, 'but ours are all 'lectric. They run off the battery. I'll light a candle, though. It's nicer.'

When he had lighted the candle in its little flat enamelled holder, Kit turned the electric light off and the cabin was immediately more cosy and homely. Both boys threw off their clothes and put on pyjamas, then roughly folded their discarded garments and stowed them in one of the cupboards. Mike helped Kit to lower the fold-down bed into position and set out the mattress and bedding before diving beneath the covers of his own little bunk. Tired though they both were, the boys chatted for a while in the soft candlelight, which cast long wobbling shadows up the sides of the cabin. They swapped the best jokes that they each knew, and had to stifle their giggles beneath the bedclothes for fear of disturbing Mrs Coleman in the butty boat.

All the while Mike was hardly able to believe that he was at last aboard one of the boats which he admired so much. His eyes could not rest, but gazed all around the interior of the tiny cabin. On the walls Vince and Kit had stuck some pictures cut out of magazines – there was a photo of the Beatles, and several more of motorbikes. Otherwise, all was very old-fashioned but cosy: the brightly painted woodwork, a colourful rag-rug on the floor, the cast-iron stove, and shiny brassware winking in the candlelight. Mike was filled with a warm glow of delight at the thought that this was now his home too.

Eventually the boys heard Mr Coleman and Vince approaching and Kit blew out the candle. Vince and his father stopped at the water's edge and stood with some of the other boatmen, talking over canal matters in low voices. One or two of the men smoked a last cigarette. The two boys strained to listen for a while, picking up bits of the men's conversation. But before long Mike was fast asleep and he did not hear Vince coming aboard, picking his way gingerly in the dark to his place beside Kit in the cross-bed.

8. Round the Magpie Pound

Mike wondered what was happening. Half-asleep, half-awake, he couldn't think where he was and suddenly felt afraid. He was in an unfamiliar bed, in a strange room and now everything around him was vibrating vigorously. But as his head cleared he remembered he was on the narrow boat, and this happy thought drove away his fear. He realised that the vibration was related to the loud noise he could hear, and that the noise was the engine of the boat, chugging away contentedly in the next compartment. Sitting up in bed and looking at his wristwatch he was surprised to see that it was only halfpast six! As he recalled the events of yesterday all the excitement of being aboard the boats returned to him afresh. He thought of Kit and glanced across at the other bed, but it was empty. There were crumpled sheets, and pillows were scattered across it, but neither Vince nor Kit was anywhere to be seen. He threw back the covers and tumbled out of his bunk.

'G'morning, sleepy-head!' said Mr Coleman, smiling, as Mike climbed up through the narrow doorway of the cabin to where Kit's dad was steering. Outside the day was already brilliant with warm sunshine that danced on the water and made it sparkle. The air was clear and fresh and the boats were underway. The wharf and the pub and the scenery of last evening were gone, left behind now, some miles distant, back down the cut. Mike drew several deep lungfuls of the sweet, cool morning air, and peering into the bright distance behind he saw *Andromeda* ploughing through the water on the end of her long line. He was beginning to wonder where Kit could be when he felt a friendly hand ruffling his tousled hair, and turning round he came face to face with his friend who grinned at him from the cabin roof.

'How long have you been up?' asked Mike, who was still rather drowsy. He was not accustomed to seeing any hour earlier than halfpast seven in the morning.

'Oh, we 'ad a lie-in today,' Kit replied, nonchalantly. 'Didn't move out of bed till just before six.'

'Don't take no notice of 'im,' said Mr Coleman. 'He's always the last one up, and even then we 'ave to kick him out of bed!'

'Let's get a wash, anyway,' said Kit. 'I've been waitin' for you. There's no locks for a while, so we can get ready and have some breakfast too.'

Inside the cabin Kit lighted a portable stove and the kettle was soon boiling. The two boys washed in a basin with a long handle like a saucepan, and which was decorated with more roses, like the water cans. 'It's called a dipper,' Kit told his friend, 'because you can dip it in the cut to get water.' Mike was reminded of camping holidays once more, only there was far less room in this compact cabin than he had ever found in a tent, and it was impossible not to splash water everywhere. 'When the boats are tied up, it's better to wash outside,' Kit apologised.

Breakfast, Mike discovered, was being cooked by Mrs Coleman aboard the butty boat and would be passed to them when ready. In the meantime there were some Corn Flakes and bread and jam aboard *Cepheus*, and the primus stove also provided hot water for tea. The process of cleansing, grooming and dressing rapidly completed, Mike and Kit reappeared on deck in time to receive a plate of bacon and egg sandwiches, passed to them by Vince. He had run along the towpath from the butty at one bridge-hole to deliver the food to them at the next. The hungry boys perched the plate on the cabin top and enjoyed their meal in the open air, to the accompaniment of the rattling engine.

Their breakfast finished, Kit and Mike remained beside Mr Coleman at the tiller. Mike noticed that they were entering a more built-up area. A lock appeared, and with it their day's work began. The first lock was followed by others spread out at distant intervals. It wasn't possible to walk quickly from one to the next as they had done on the previous day, so Vince took a bicycle off at a bridge-hole and sped away down the path to prepare the locks ahead of the boats, leaving his mother to steer *Andromeda*. Mike and Kit jumped off as they reached each lock and helped the boats through, whilst Vince remounted and pedalled on to the next one. His old bike lacked mudguards, lights and other customary bicycle parts. But it was well-made and sturdy, and withstood the frequent potholes and the rough, stony surface of the ill-kempt path. Vince pedalled furiously along, pretending he was on a powerful BSA or Triumph motorbike.

Mike now had his own windlass. Mr Coleman had found a spare one in the engine room and had cleaned it up and made it shine, giving it a good scrub with some wire wool and paraffin. Mike kept this 'iron' tucked into his belt as Kit had shown him, and he was very proud of it because it was his 'badge of office'; it showed that he was now a Boy of 'The Cut'. By ten o'clock the boats had reached a town and were gliding between an odd mixture of scenery – high walls, the backs of factories and warehouses; rubbish tips, derelict buildings and colourful back gardens. Here and there the boats were momentarily enveloped in the dark shadows of some overhanging wharfs and a wide bridge.

Mike spotted buses and pedestrians passing along the busy main road as it crossed the canal in the centre of the town. His first thought was that he might wave to passers-by, but no one seemed to notice the still, murky water below the bridge, or the painted craft that chugged by with their cargo and crew. The people looked straight ahead, or were absorbed in conversation as they walked. One woman, pushing a pram, was trying at the same time to keep another child from wandering into the path of the traffic. The traffic roared, horns tooted, and Mike found that everyone was preoccupied; the noisy town was getting on with its daily business whilst the canal passed silently beneath, unobserved and ignored. Indeed the town seemed to show only contempt for the old waterway, since its folk had seen fit to dispose of their rubbish along the banks and even in the cut itself.

'We'll have to be careful of junk on the bottom,' said Mr Coleman, as he slowed the engine right down. 'Don't want another set of springs on the blades like Vince 'ad last week.'

They slid gently beneath the bridge and on past the gasworks. Huge drum-shaped gas-holders, red with rust, loomed over the cut. Mike saw a churchyard where mounds of dead flowers, piled against a wall, had spilled over onto the canal path. Then the buildings gradually thinned out, the walls gave way to hedgerows, and fields and woodland appeared once again. The country was more undulating here and the waterway began to twist and turn in broad curves. Not long after they had left the town and entered this hilly landscape Kit started to get very agitated, and looking ahead Mike could see that the canal was approaching a dark and shapeless mass of trees and undergrowth.

'We're coming to the creepy bit,' Kit shouted to Mike excitedly. 'Let's go up the fore-end.'

'Be careful, Kit!' his father warned, but Kit was already climbing onto the cabin roof, beckoning to Mike to follow him.

'Take it easy, Mike,' Kit's dad spoke firmly. 'You'd better go on all fours at first.'

The black tarpaulins that cover the cargo of narrow boats come up almost to a point, forming a ridge right down the centre of the boat. The ridge itself is a narrow pathway, about nine inches wide, shaped by the long planks that lie beneath the tarpaulins. As if he were a cat tripping along the ridge of a house roof, Kit now sped down this planking to the front of the boat. Mike followed, but had to tread very carefully, and bent forward so that he could hold on with his hands. On each side the dull black fabric fell away to the gunwales of the boat, and if he had lost his footing Mike felt sure that he would have tumbled straight off the side and into the water. So it took him a moment or two to reach the front of the boat – the fore-end – where Kit had already climbed down onto the little triangular deck above the bows.

'That was a bit dodgy,' said Mike, who was relieved to have arrived safely, and could still feel the butterflies in his stomach. 'I wish you'd warned me we were gonna do some acrobatics!'

'Sorry,' said Kit. 'I run up and down the boats all the time. I s'pose it looks a bit dangerous if you 'aven't done it before.' Mike's main thought was that he would have to go back the same way later, but he was also aware that his friend was quite excited now and felt that something weird or wonderful was about to happen.

The two boys sat one each side of the boat, with their feet stretched out over the bows. The warmth of the sun-baked metal under their legs was comforting, and with the engine far behind them they could hear the gentle slap, slapping of the water as the bows sliced into the glassy surface. Mike soon felt the warmth of the day draining away, however, as if the evening had come early. A chill came into the air, and though the sunlight still shone brightly high overhead, it was as if it shone in another world. The scene around them was gloomy and dark. Woods crowded in and only shadows could be seen between the trunks of the trees, clustered densely about the waterside. Long tangled vines trailed down from overhanging branches, some reaching right to the water. There were many dead trees, whose skeletal forms, twisted as if in pain, leaned at wild angles towards one another, or over the cut. They seemed to strain as though to escape from something, yet remained rooted in the murky banks. All smelt dank and mouldy, of rotting vegetation and stagnant water.

'No one ever ties up here at night,' said Kit. 'It's called the Magpie Pound. We all make sure we stop before we gets 'ere, or else we works on till we're well past it.'

'What's wrong with the place?' Mike asked, although he already had goose pimples breaking out on his arms. He began to feel nervous and peered into the eerie depths of the woods, not certain whether he hadn't seen, from the corner of his eye, some dark shapes darting about in the shadows. When he looked again he saw only the tangle of fallen branches and lumpy clumps of marsh grass around black pools of water, glimpsed between the crowded trunks.

'Spooks!' said Kit, letting the horror of the word sink in before adding, 'And Will o' the Wisps, and spirits, and things that scare yer, and chase yer and keep yer awake at night.'

'You don't believe all that sort of talk, do you?' said Mike. He tried to sound cocky and scornful but thought that, in this eerie place, he could very well believe it himself. At that moment a couple of jet-black rooks started up suddenly within the wood. Their ragged wings clattered loudly in the silence, breaking the uncanny stillness and startling both boys on the boat, so that they nearly fell off the front. The sudden racket set off a general commotion, and several pigeons and other creatures were put to flight. For a moment the whole wood seemed alive with the sound of rustling branches, snapping twigs and animals scuttling through the undergrowth. Then the noise subsided and all was still again.

'I dunno what I believe,' Kit replied, in a far-away sort of voice. For the canal people had their traditions and folklore and Mike now regretted his last remark. He realised that he ought to respect his friend's feelings and not make fun of what Kit was saying. 'All I can say is, I've heard the stories,' Kit went on. 'Like the one about the great dog what carried off young children from a boat, many years ago, an' disappeared into these woods, an' was never seen again. And there's the tale of the young woman that people hear calling at night, and who they say is the ghost of Lucy Mumford, who was chased into the cut by something terrible. She never rests now, but calls out to warn others of the danger.'

'Stop it, Kit!' shouted Mike, who was beginning to feel really scared. Shivers went down his back, and he felt distinctly cold. 'I don't believe in ghosts,' he said firmly, '– but I don't like this place either.'

'Well, I didn't mean to scare yer,' said Kit, ' but you *did* ask me!'

A hoot, like an owl, came eerily from a distance and made them jump again. Their conversation came to a halt. Then Kit smiled, and sprang up.

'I know it's you, Vince, so you can shut up!' he shouted into the gloom where *Andromeda* followed behind. 'I thought it was Vince, trying to frighten us,' he said, turning to Mike with a puzzled expression. But Vince was too far away to have been heard. The two boys stared at each other in silence.

The spooky stretch of canal continued for another half a mile. It wound to left and right so that it was difficult to see when it would come to an end. Each bend revealed only another vista of shades and dark water in which no reflections appeared. The boys talked of cheerful things and tried to make each other laugh. But all the while they were glancing furtively into the shadows, dreading that they might see something hideous lurking amongst the ivy-clad tree trunks; fearing that cold clammy hands might suddenly grasp their shoulders.

After what seemed hours, but was barely ten minutes, the air warmed, the gloom came to an end and the landscape opened out again into rolling fields. Cattle and sheep grazed peacefully in pastures, and there were cornfields golden and ripe, awaiting the harvester. A tower here and a spire there marked distant villages. Mike and Kit relaxed as the eerie sensations faded and the strange wooded landscape was left behind.

They remained together on the fore-end of *Cepheus*, and from their vantage point observed some familiar creatures of the cut. Standing solemnly beside the water they saw the great grey heron with his impossibly long thin neck and his pale breast flecked with black like an ermine robe. On his spindly legs he was still as a sentinel, waiting patiently for his prey, the unwary fish. As the boats drew near to him he would lean slowly forward, spread his huge wings and, flying low over the water, move up to a new perch some yards ahead. Once again the boat would draw near to him, and once again he flapped away up the cut, casting his great shadow over the rippled surface.

Everywhere along the cut were mallard ducks, the females a speckled brown with white flashes on their wings, the males brightly coloured with bottle-green necks. The mother duck often had a flotilla of tiny chicks clustered around her. How she flapped and fussed if her flock became separated, some on one side of a passing boat, some on the other. And how the fluffy little babies cheeped till the boats were gone by and they could see their mother once more. The ducks were glad of the passing boats however, because stale crusts and other titbits were sometimes thrown from them. They would swim eagerly towards approaching craft, looking for a free meal. The mallards shared the water with the shyer, white-crested coots and the green-legged moorhens, which kept to the margins when the boats passed by.

All at once Kit's excited cry drew Mike's attention to a streak of lustrous blue that skimmed the surface of the water. He had hardly glimpsed it before it disappeared into the trees. It was a kingfisher. 'Never mind,' said Kit, 'I 'spect you'll see another one soon. They're lovely birds, but they're so quick. You don't have long to look at 'em before they're gone.' Mike asked Kit to remind him later of the birds they'd seen so that he could look them up in his bird book.

As they glided along Kit told his friend more about the canals and the boats. He pointed out the path that ran continuously beside the cut. This was called the towpath, he explained, because before the days of engines all the boats were hauled by horses or mules, which towed them from the bank on long ropes. It was unusual to see a horse boat these days, Kit said, though there were still a few. One of the last had been run by old Mr and Mrs Skinner with their mule 'Dolly', and Kit had met them a few times, still at work, when he was a small boy.

Boats had engines today, Kit went on, except when they were butties and were paired with a motor. Butties were made in the form of the traditional horse-drawn boats; but motor boats were a different shape, and had a rounded stern called a counter, beneath which the propeller turned.

Mike was familiar with locks by now, and understood how they both raised and lowered the canal as it crossed the landscape. This was the main difference between the artificial canals and the natural rivers which, though some had locks, made a gentle descent as they flowed to the ocean. The still waters of the canals went far inland, and as they crossed the uplands they linked together some of the grea t rivers: Thames and Severn, Trent and Mersey. In this way boats like *Andromeda* and *Cepheus* could carry cargoes all over the country. Kit explained how the canal was sometimes cut straight through a hillside in a tunnel, in order to save a lot of hard work on many locks. To Mike's delight Kit said there would be two long tunnels on this trip, and that he would see the first one the following day. 'You'll love it,' said Kit to his friend. 'The tunnels are even more exciting than the creepy place!' he added with a grin.

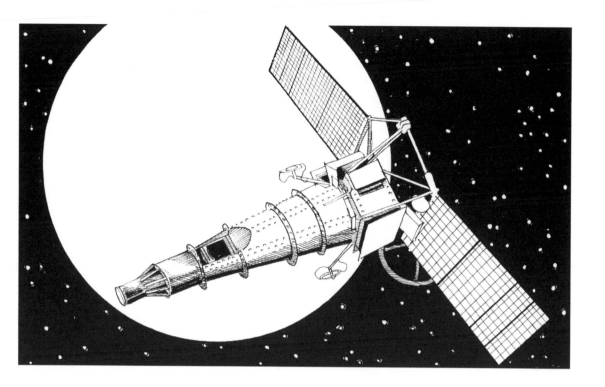

9. Moon Rockets and Gas Lamps

Late that afternoon the two narrow boats were travelling round a long pound with no locks, which meant there was little work to be done. Mike was on the butty boat talking to Mrs Coleman; Kit was steering *Andromeda* to give his brother a break and Vince was resting in their cabin on *Cepheus*. Susannah was also aboard the motor with her dad, reading the newspaper to him as they went along. Mr Coleman could only read very slowly and felt embarrassed when he had to spend such a long time on each page of the paper. It was good for Susie to practise her reading and it also helped to pass the time when she read to him on the move.

Mike liked being on the butty now and then, because it was much quieter than the motor. The engine, separated from them by the length of the long line, was reduced to a distant popping. On *Andromeda* you could hear the water swishing around the hull of the boat and gurgling past the great rudder – or the 'elum' as the boaters called it – and you didn't need to raise your voice to talk. Mike was enjoying the peace now, and at the same time he felt envious of Kit at the tiller and wished that he would soon be taught how to steer too. But he knew that, although he was gradually learning to become part of the team, it was still early days and so he tried to be content with whatever job he was given.

As Mike talked to Kit's mum his humble but important job this afternoon was peeling the potatoes for their tea. In the cabin, neatly arranged in a jam jar, were some flowers. 'Did you grow those yourself?' asked Mike, who didn't know much about flowers and didn't recall seeing any flowerpots around the boats.

'Dear me, no!' cried Mrs Coleman, laughing. 'I don't have time to do any gardening. But we have as big a garden as anyone could wish for,' she added, smiling at Mike, who looked at her quizzically. So she explained how wild flowers grew naturally all along the cut, and that if they wanted fresh blooms to decorate the boats, they had only to step off at a lock or bridge-hole to find armfuls of them beside the towpath.

'These big white ones are moon daisies,' she said, and began pointing out the individual flowers. 'This is red campion, and there's some Ragged Robin. This pink one's mallow, this fluffy one is burdock, and these tall fellows are rosebay willowherb. You'll see huge clumps of that, all along the cut, and in the autumn it turns into lots of white hairy seeds, and we call it "Old Man's Beard".'

'Oh yes, I remember that,' said Mike, who had heard some of the names of wild flowers from his dad on country walks, but had never really taken a lot of notice.

'An' there's fruit too, of course,' went on Mrs Coleman. 'We can stock up our larder from the hedgerows as well. The blackberries have started already, and one night soon we'll have a bramble pie for our pudding, with custard. Then there's crab apples for jam or jelly; and elderberries – they're very good for making cordial, lots of vitamin C, very good for you. And then there's sloes – I often pick a few of them to make some sloe gin, as a special treat for Christmas.' Mike had never heard of sloe gin, but it sounded very attractive. Mrs Coleman explained how it was made by adding the fruit to a bottle of the spirit, and how the berries flavoured the gin and made it sweet and syrupy. It was only to be drunk in small measures, she added – and wasn't really for youngsters. 'You stick with the elderberry cordial,' she said, 'that'll keep you healthy!'

Mike had nearly finished his peeling and was gazing around the cabin. 'Is that you and Mr Coleman?' he asked, nodding at a small black and white photograph in a wooden frame which swung gently on its nail.

'Which one? Oh yes! That's Dick and me on our wedding day in 1945. Didn't we make a lovely couple!'

'Mmmm,' murmured Mike, nodding his head and thinking that Mrs Coleman still looked pretty now. Though her life was hard he felt that she was more relaxed, more easy-going than his own mum, who often seemed to be worried and fretful with the cares of life, and this had made lines in her face. She was always busy finding something to do around the house too, and they didn't often sit and talk as he was talking now with Kit's mum. He rather wished that he could have done this at home. Perhaps he would try, he thought, when he got back.

That evening they tied up on the outskirts of a small town. There was no pub nearby, but a busy street could be seen between the old brick warehouses near their mooring. After tea Mr Coleman wandered off to see if he could find any of his friends in a pub in the town. Vince set to work on a model of a motorbike that he had been making for some weeks. He wanted to be left in peace on the motor, so Mike and Kit remained with Susannah and Mrs Coleman on the butty where they listened to the wireless.

The news programme was all about the Ranger 7 moon explorer. Mike remembered the TV reports when it had reached the moon a few weeks ago, and had begun sending lots of photographs back to earth. Now the Americans were talking about their Apollo 'Man to the Moon' programme, and how they hoped actually to land a man on the moon in a rocket before 1970. Everyone in the little cabin listened in disbelief to these fantastic plans. Mike thought what a strange contrast it was. As the scientists talked about exploring space, and the amazing technology being developed, he was sitting here on this old-fashioned form of transport, which had hardly changed in two hundred years. A coal fire glowed between the bars of the cast-iron range on which their meals had been cooked and now the kettle on top of it was singing softly. Outside there were gas lamps ready to brighten up the cobbled yard when dusk eventually fell over the deserted warehouses. There would be no moon to be seen tonight, it was too cloudy. But even if he could have seen it, Mike decided, it would still be difficult to imagine men walking around on it.

Mike thought of his mum and how she would now be hurrying to one of her friends down the road to watch *Coronation Street* on the telly. And here was he, with a family who managed quite well without television, or a refrigerator, or a motor car, or many of the things that he took for granted at home. This was certainly a different life, a very special life, far removed from the world of satellites and space rockets. He admitted to himself that he missed his mum and dad. He didn't miss them because he was homesick, but mainly because he would have liked them to share his excitement. He wanted to show them the canal and tell them all about the boats and everything that he had learned. Apart from that he was perfectly content and he hoped that his new way of life could go on forever.

'You'd better give your mum a ring tonight, Mike,' said Mrs Coleman, as if she had heard his thoughts. 'There'll be a phone box nearby, on the main street. If you go up with our Kit and Susie I'll give you all some money to buy a bottle of pop.'

'Thanks very much,' said Mike, and he climbed over onto *Cepheus* to dig out his tobacco tin of coins for the telephone. 'Careful, Mike!' shouted Vince, whose hands were awkwardly poised with bits of motorbike and a tube of glue. 'Don't rock the boat!' 'Sorry, Vince!' Mike replied. He returned to *Andromeda* as stealthily as a cat, but missed his footing and grabbed at the handrail on *Cepheus*, setting the craft in motion again. Mike darted into the butty cabin, ignoring Vince's muffled curses from the other boat.

The three children washed all the plates and pots and stowed everything carefully away before going out. Then together they ran up the alley between the warehouses and found a red telephone kiosk close by on the street.

Susannah and Kit had to help Mike as he struggled with the door on its strong spring. It slammed shut behind him as soon as he was inside, and in his strange red prison he was aware of the warmth through the glass panels. There was a strong smell of print and paper from the fat directory that lay on its shelf, and an aroma of tobacco left by a previous caller. Out of habit he checked the little metal hopper at the bottom of the phone in case someone had forgotten to collect their returned coins. No luck this time, however. He lifted the heavy black receiver and put his money into the slot before dialling.

'Hullo,' said Mike, when someone answered at the other end of the line and he hastily pressed the button marked 'A'. He heard his coin clatter into the metal box as he asked, 'Is that Mrs Aldridge?' His neighbour seemed pleased to hear him, and after quickly enquiring whether he was having a good time she asked him to hold on while she hurried next door to fetch someone. Within a few moments Mike heard his mother's familiar voice and they spent several minutes sharing news until the operator warned that his money was running out. Mike gabbled, 'got to go now, Mum – don't worry, I'm having a really fab time. I'll call again soon. Say hello to Dad. Bye!'

Susannah and Kit had been making faces at him through the glass panes of the kiosk. Now he pushed at the heavy door and ran out into the fresh evening air to join them. He followed as they led the way down the road to a little off-licence next to a pub called the 'Star and Garter'. All the other shops were closed by this time, but the window of this little store was still brightly lit. Mike found it exciting to be in a different place again this evening. It was one of the best things about travelling on the boats; you were in new surroundings all the time yet you always had your home with you, close by. He was enjoying being a stranger in this town, and exploring its streets and alleyways; and later there would be the boats waiting for him, and his cosy bed in the cabin of *Cepheus*.

But although the town was strange to Mike it seemed to be familiar territory to the others. In fact Kit and Susannah had been to this little shop many times before and knew well its racks of sweets, boxes of potato crisps and rows of bottled beer and soft drinks. A bell rang as they pushed open the door. 'Hullo, Mr Dobinson!' the children cried cheerily as the proprietor appeared in response to the silvery tinkle. The bell continued to swing on its spring above the door.

'What can I do for you, young Colemans?' Mr Dobinson replied. 'And how's your mum and dad, and the big lad?'

'Oh, they're all fine, thanks very much. Can we 'ave a bottle of pop, please? Have you got any Dandelion and Burdock?' Mr Dobinson wasn't old, probably about fifty. He had lost most of his hair, though, and what was left was combed in thin brown strands across the top of his balding head. He was rather short and rotund and wore a pair of thick-framed spectacles with strong lenses, which magnified his eyes alarmingly when he looked straight at you. Deftly he ran his hands over a long line of 'Corona' pop bottles, murmuring to himself, 'Lemonade . . . Cherryade . . . Cream Soda . . . Ginger Beer . . . ah! Dandelion and Burdock. Here we are. Just the one bottle was it?'

The children handed over a couple of coins and in the conversation that followed they introduced Mike to Mr Dobinson. 'You're a lucky lad,' he said, bending his face towards Mike across the counter, his eyes suddenly bulging through his glasses as if to give Mike an extra-thorough inspection. 'You couldn't have found a nicer family on the boats; you'll be well looked after! I hope you have a really good holiday.' And then he addressed all the children, 'Perhaps I'll see you next week, on your way back?' And after another exchange of pleasantries Kit and Susannah promised to pass on his regards to their parents and the three of them pushed in a huddle through the door.

'Don't forget there's sixpence on the bottle!' Mr Dobinson called after them, and they waved to him as they set off back to the boats.

'We can get extra pocket money by collecting bottles,' said Susannah. 'People take pop with them along the towpath when they're out for walks or picnics, and they just throw the empties in the bushes. Sometimes we can find ten or a dozen in a week, and that makes us five or six bob!'

Chatting happily, the three children hurried back down the street. There were few people about – a man was taking his dog for a walk and two young women were laughing together arm in arm, on their way home from work. Kit started a solo game of football, kicking an empty tin can down the street, and he got ahead of the others. He was the first to reach the entrance to the narrow lane that led back to the warehouses where the boats were tied. But as he turned the corner into the alley he suddenly froze in his tracks. Mike and Susannah looked at each other with puzzled expressions before hurrying towards him to see what was up.

10. A Narrow Escape

'Where d'you think you're going, Carrot-Top?' a loud voice said. The voice belonged to the largest boy in a group of teenagers who were standing a few yards into the lane. With them were some smaller children, about Susannah's age. There were probably only eight or nine kids altogether, but as they milled around they looked like a crowd. The boy with the loud voice was tough-looking, tall and broad-shouldered. Dressed in blue jeans and a crisply ironed checked shirt, on his feet were smart 'winkle-picker' shoes, with toes that went to a point. Perhaps he fancied himself as James Dean or some other cocky young man he'd seen in films. He certainly looked threatening to Kit, Mike and Susannah. The boy was smoking a cigarette, which he passed now and then to one of the smaller boys, whose face reddened as he stifled a cough. This rather spoiled his attempt at looking 'hard'.

'This is our alley, and NO ONE goes down it – especially dirty little kids like you.' This was another of the teenagers, a girl this time, who had some difficulty in speaking because she was chewing bubblegum. She then blew a large translucent pink bubble, to demonstrate how cool and clever she was. When it burst with a sharp smack onto her face, she simply drew it back into her mouth and carried on chewing.

The children instinctively looked back to see if there was a means of escape, but some of the gang had already walked round behind them, blocking off their retreat.

'Get out the way!' Kit demanded, in as strong a voice as he could manage, though he was feeling very uncomfortable. He didn't know Mike well enough yet to know whether he would stick up for him if it came to a fight; and he was most concerned about Susannah, that she should not get hurt. The gang didn't look especially nasty, but there were a lot of them.

'You're not goin' anywhere unless we say so, Carrot-Top!' the first bully said, calmly blowing smoke rings into the air. 'Where are you off to anyway?'

'None of your business!' This was Mike, who now stood shoulder to shoulder with Kit whilst Susannah hid behind them, pressing herself into their backs.

'It's the rats from off the barges!' shouted one of the smaller children.

'Smelly rats! Smelly rats!' the other youngsters began to chant, and they jumped up and down gleefully, feeling safe in the company of the teenagers.

'They're Gyppoes!' shouted somebody else.

'Smelly rats! smelly rats!' the horrible voices taunted.

'Gyppoes, dirty Gyppoes!'

'Look at their funny clothes!' came a voice.

'Look at those baggy trousers' came another. 'Where did yer get them from, the rag bag?' And they all laughed, and chanted again, 'Smelly rats! smelly rats!'

'Shut up, shut up!' shouted Susannah, running out from behind the boys to confront the big girl herself. 'Shut them up, or I'll kick you!'

'The boys scared are they?' the girl sneered. 'Had to send the tiddler out to stand up for them?'

'We're not scared,' said Kit, taking a step forward. He felt reassured when Mike stepped boldly forward with him and added, 'Yeah, we're not scared!' – though in reality his legs felt like jelly and his stomach seemed to turn itself inside out.

'Come 'ere and get yer 'ead smacked, then,' said the first bully. 'Bet yer won't!'

All the eyes of the smaller children now boggled with excitement, but nobody moved.

'Give us your pop, then,' said the girl, as each group eyed the other and the tension grew. 'We're all thirsty. We could do with a little drink, couldn't we, Kev?' and she turned for approval to the big bully, whom she obviously admired.

'Couldn't we everybody?' she shouted to the general assembly of followers, and they all nodded at her.

'And it's sixpence each to pass.' This remark came from one of the smaller children, who stepped forward importantly, holding out a grimy hand.

'No! It's a *shilling* for Gyppoes!' shouted another, boldly.

'Yeah, a shillin' each,' said the big girl, 'and your bottle of pop, or you're not going anywhere.' And she placed her hands on her hips and fixed them all with an ugly scowl.

'Just try it, that's all,' said Kit, clutching the bottle of Dandelion and Burdock close to his stomach. Then, with a look of thunder on his face, and a note of defiance in his voice, he said, 'If you wan' it – come an' ged it!'

It was all or nothing now. The gang began to close in on the children, who stood in a huddle, tensed and ready for whatever was about to happen. Kit's hands were full, because he had the bottle – though he had an idea that he might use it as a cudgel. Mike felt he ought to make a show of strength by putting his fists up to the crowd – or something, but he couldn't make up his mind. Susannah was frightened but was trying not to cry.

'Oi! Give it back!'

The sudden cry came from one of the teenage girls who had been standing at the back of the gang, holding the handlebars of her shiny new bicycle. It was a beautiful machine, bright lilac in colour with a white plastic basket on the front. Colourful streamers fluttered from the handlebar grips, and there was a special plastic guard on the rear wheel to prevent flapping skirts from getting tangled in the spokes.

'Give me back my bike!' the girl screamed. All the gang turned round to see what was happening, and there stood Vince, holding the glittering bicycle aloft. He had set out from the boats to see what had become of Kit, Susannah and Mike, because it was a while since they had left for the shop. Hearing shouting in the alley as he approached, and recognising Susannah's voice, he had crept up unseen and carefully weighed up the situation. Deciding he had to take the gang by surprise he had quickly formed his plan, and it had been an easy matter to leap forward and snatch the bicycle from the startled girl's grasp.

'Let them through, or the bike goes in the cut!' Vince shouted, backing off slowly towards the end of the alley and the canal.

'Oh, you're so hard!' shouted Kevin, the biggest bully. 'Give the bike back NOW, or I'll smack you one,' and he began to sidle down the narrow passage. His right hand strayed towards his back pocket and Mike thought he was going to produce a flick-knife. He looked really menacing.

But Vince stood his ground. 'Let them through,' he said again, quietly and calmly this time, 'or . . .' and he turned to signal his intention by glancing towards the water.

Mike, Kit and Susannah began to edge their way through the gang, who were rooted to the spot, like statues. They all gazed open-mouthed at Vince, and at the bicycle which he still held in the air as he slowly paced backwards. Even the bubblegum girl had stopped chewing, and her mouth gaped in amazement. From his back pocket the bully coolly pulled out a packet of cigarettes, and lit another fag.

The three children reached Vince, and as they passed he jerked his head, silently indicating that they should go on and make their way straight back to the boats. 'Now clear off, all of you!' he said to the crowd.

'I want my bike back!' sobbed the teenage girl. 'It's brand new. My dad will kill me if it gets damaged.'

'Clear off . . . !' Vince shouted again, standing now at the water's edge, '. . . or the bike goes in the cut.'

The small children scattered first, running in all directions so that they bumped into each other, and two of them fell over. They were followed by the teenagers – who walked nonchalantly away, hands in pockets, as if they were not at all bothered. The sobbing girl remained, though she took several steps backwards as if she meant to leave. And the big bully still stood in the middle of the alley, glowering at Vince. 'I dare you!' he said. Vince began to swing the bicycle as if he were taking aim for the very middle of the cut.

'Go away, Kev! I want my bike back,' the girl pleaded with the bully, and Vince swung the bike again. The boy thought for a moment before sucking heavily one last time on his cigarette and tossing it to the ground. Then, exhaling smoke aggressively between his gritted teeth, he backed off, turned and swaggered down the alley and away.

'Here's yer bike!' Vince snapped. Then, as if he were ticking off a whole crowd of kids, he added, 'You're lucky you didn't have to fish it out of the cut. And DON'T let me catch you causin' trouble round here again!' Vince felt a little sorry for the poor girl as he unleashed his anger at her; she had really only been a bystander. But she was the only one of the gang left, and he felt he had to shout at somebody. He placed the bicycle carefully onto some grass beside the towpath, then walked away. Glancing back he saw the girl rush to recover her property and, climbing quickly onto the saddle, wobble her way up the uneven surface of the alley and disappear round the corner.

Back on *Andromeda* the three friends shared their pop and laughed with sheer relief after their lucky rescue and escape.

'Good old Vince!' said Susannah, 'The Cavalry arrived just in the nick of time!'

'Good old Vince,' the two boys agreed.

'It was lucky for that big bloke,' boasted Mike, emboldened now that the danger was past. 'I was just about to sock him one.'

'*I* was, you mean,' cried Kit, indignantly. 'He was about to get this bottle over his 'ead . . .'

'None of you was going to hit him,' said Susannah, jumping into the conversation quickly. 'We were lucky that Vince came along when he did.' And suddenly the others fell quiet, because they knew that Susannah was right. Neither of them wanted to think what might have happened if Vince had not come looking for them.

Then the children felt the boat rock, and Vince himself stepped down into the cabin. 'They won't be bothering us again for a while!' he said cheerily, slapping his hands together as if removing the dust of battle from them. 'Any of that pop left?'

The others had saved a share of the Dandelion and Burdock for Vince, and they now fell over each other to be first to get him a cup and pour it out.

'Okay, okay!' laughed the older lad. 'I know I'm the great hero, but you don't have to make such a big fuss.'

'Thanks, Vince,' Kit said meekly. 'You were brilliant.'

'I don't know what would have happened if you hadn't shown up,' said Mike.

'It's what big brothers are for,' Vince went on, and added, 'So, what are we gonna to do tonight then, kids? – and where's me mum gone?'

Mrs Coleman had gone out to chat with the women on another pair of boats tied up further along the canal. The younger children were pleased that Vince seemed to want to stay with them, rather than follow his dad to the pub.

'We were gonna play some games,' said Susannah. 'What would you like to play, Vince?'

'How about Hangman?'

'Yeah!' the others cried. 'An' Battleships!' shouted Mike.

'Yeah – and Consequences!' shouted Susannah.

Excitedly the children searched for scraps of paper and pencils, Vince tuned the wireless to a pirate station playing the Top Twenty, and they began their simple but engaging games. There was a lot of chatter and laughter and Vince was pleased because the others seemed to have forgotten all about their unpleasant encounter in the alley. It was a warm evening, and the embers in the stove made the cabin hotter still, though the doors and the sliding hatch were open. Sitting crowded round the little drop-down table, absorbed in their games, they hardly noticed the time pass. But the cloudy sky turned through darker shades of grey to black, and the air grew chill. A moth flew in and fluttered helplessly around the bright light.

11. An Old Boaters' Tale

'Time for cocoa!' said Vince at last, as their games came to an end. He flicked the wireless off and silence fell over the cabin. Carefully the tall lad extricated himself from his seat and the others all shuffled around to let him get near the stove, where he made a clatter with saucepans, milk bottles, tins and mugs.

'Wonder where me mum's got to,' Kit mused.

''Spect she's like us,' Susannah replied. 'She's been so busy talking that she hasn't noticed the time.'

'Well, when we've finished this we'll all get off to our cabin,' Vince said, and soon he and the others were sipping their warming cups of the rich chocolate drink. The biscuit tin was passed round, and after rummaging amongst the assortment to find one of his favourite lemon creams Kit brought up the subject of the next day's journey.

'Mike's gonna love the tunnels, isn't he, Vince?'

'They're very scary,' said Susannah, with a shudder. 'I don't like them.'

'If you've never been through one before,' Vince said to Mike, 'then there's nothing like it – you wait an' see. I think they're fantastic, especially when you think that they're two hundred years old and were built before the days of mechanical diggers and drills, and all that. It must have taken ages and ages to finish 'em.' But having said this much Vince could not be persuaded to enthral them with more talk. He was not in the mood any more, and finishing his cocoa he said goodnight to them all and crept out into the dusk.

Mike yawned and, though tomorrow held exciting prospects, even Kit – who liked to stay up and talk as late as possible – was finding it harder and harder to think of things to say. The conversation flagged and Mike could feel his bed calling him. Then there came a gentle pitter-patter on the roof of the cabin – it had begun to rain. The sound grew steadily faster and louder as the shower became a heavy downpour. Kit and Mike decided to make a run for it before it got worse. With a quick 'Goodnight!' to Susannah they hastily clambered across the wet sterns of the boats and tumbled into their cabin, drawing the cabin slide right across the top of the doors to keep out the wet. Soon a real storm was brewing and the drumming on the roof sounded more like ball bearings than raindrops. Vince was in bed. He was reading the adventures of Dan Dare, the astronaut, in an old *Eagle* annual bought at a jumble sale. The drama of the rain and the thunder had made the younger boys quite excited, and now they no longer felt sleepy but were wide awake.

'Read us a story, Vince, please,' asked Kit as he put on his pyjamas and scrambled into the bed beside his brother,' – or tell us one of the old ones.'

'It'll have to be a short one, I wanna sleep soon,' said Vince, 'and the noise of this rain won't help.' But the older boy, who usually liked to think of himself as very grown up and 'one of the men', was happy to oblige his younger brother.

In fact, Vince was very skilled at story-telling – probably because he had had so many stories told to him as a small child, by his parents and by other boat people that the family knew. Tales of old boatmen and the days of boating long ago had been mixed with ghost stories, humorous tales and gory accounts of misfortunes and accidents; stories passed down through generations of boaters by word of mouth. Vince, and later Kit and Susannah, had always listened spellbound to these old tales and would often ask for their favourite ones to be told again and again.

'Tell Mike the one about Lucy Mumford,' said Kit, with a grin; and then, in a spooky voice, 'It's a Dark and Stormy Night . . . just right for a little ghost story!'

'Not the story from that scary place we passed today?' asked Mike, anxiously. The moment Kit had mentioned the name of Lucy Mumford all the dread of that sinister stretch of water had come flooding back into his mind.

'Yep! That's the one,' said Kit cheerfully, adding with a leer, 'You'll love it!' But Mike wasn't so sure.

So Vince began to recount what was one of their favourites of the old tales, whilst the two younger boys snuggled down deeper into their bedding. The rain had cooled the air and they were glad of their warm blankets that night. But with bedclothes drawn up tightly around his chin, Mike also felt a little more secure from spooks and spectres.

Vince lay back on his pillows, his arms folded across his chest. 'It all happened a long time ago,' he began, gazing blankly up at the ceiling as he settled comfortably into his story-telling. 'Daniel Mumford and his young wife hadn't been married long, and their boat was a new one, and they'd called it *Sophia* after Lucy's mother. Everything was going well for them, and life seemed rich and good. Until one autumn night, when they had to tie up early in the Magpie Pound because the fog had come up really thick and they couldn't see where they was going. Soon it was dark as well, and because they were far from any village or farm, they decided to turn in straight after their tea and make an early start in the morning.

'Well, not long after they had put out their lamp, and were snuggled down in their bed – just like we all are now – up jumps Lucy, scared as anything, and she shakes her husband beside her in the bed. "Mumford," she whispers, "what's that noise?" "I don't know, dear, I didn't hear nothing," he says. "Go back to sleep."

'But Lucy was wide awake, and scared, and soon she hears the noise again. A sniffing sound, like a dog snuffling at the doors of the hatches, as if it wanted to come in. And then, after the snuffling, a scratching noise, like the creature was pawing at the doors to get them open.

'"There it is again," says Lucy. "Something's outside the cabin, trying to get in!" "I still didn't hear a thing," says her husband, "but, if it will put your mind at rest, dear, I'll have a look outside." So up he gets, opens the doors and peers out. It is still thick fog outside, and everything around the boat is as still and quiet as anything. "Nothing out here," he says to his wife, and he climbs back into bed.

'But only moments later, Lucy cries out again. She's heard the snuffling at the doors, and this time a low growling noise as well, and more scratching. The scratching is so loud, she thinks the creature is about to burst the doors open and jump in. "It's back," she screams out, and this time she's scared out of her wits and clings to her husband with an iron grip.

'Daniel Mumford still hasn't heard a thing, but seeing that his wife is really terrified he says to her, "All right, my love, I'll go and see what it is and we'll chase it off, eh?" And he puts on his clothes, and pulls on his boots, and grabs his iron in case . . .' Vince paused. 'Well, just in case! There's nothing to be seen when he opens the doors, so he climbs out of the hatches and steps off the boat.

'Soon as he's gone, Lucy Mumford is seized by a panic, 'cause she's been left on her own in the boat. What if the creature should come back while Daniel is away? So without thinking, she flies out of the cabin, bare feet, nightdress and all, and jumps onto the towpath shouting, "Wait for me! Don't leave me!"

'But the fog is thicker than ever and she can't see a thing. Daniel has walked towards the fore-end of the boat, but Lucy sets off down the towpath in the other direction. Daniel turns round when he hears her shouting "Wait for me!" but he can't see her. He begins to run in the direction of her voice, and with his arms outstretched in front of him he stumbles blindly along on the dark and foggy path.

'Suddenly a fallen branch trips him up and he sprawls in the wet grass – lucky he didn't fall into the cut. But just as he is picking himself up he hears from the murky dense fog in the distance a horrible howling, like a dog in pain, a long piercing wail that hangs in the air around him. His blood runs cold, the hair on his neck tingles, and he feels like he's been turned to stone; he can't move a muscle.

'When the eerie howling dies away he hears another sound, the sound of someone screaming and screaming. The sound is very distant, but he realises that it must be his Lucy. Now he finds his strength again, and lifts himself up; but before he has had a chance to put one foot in front of the other there comes another sound, a big splash, like something – or someone – falling into the water. "Lucy!" he shouts, and now he is really terrified. In the darkness he forgets all care for his own safety and fairly sprints along the pathway. Then all of a sudden a huge black shape looms up in front of him. He stops, and falls to his knees, and as he sprawls on the muddy path he hears the sound of padded feet pounding towards him, pounding, pounding. And then the great black shadow flies past him in the fog and the sound of the pounding feet fades away behind him.

'He realises that all his hair is standing on end, and he's shivering with cold, and the air around him has become like ice. He's so scared he begins to cry, and it is a long time before he can pull himself together. Gradually he crawls forward, picks himself up and stumbles along, still calling his wife's name, though his voice is very faint and he can hardly speak.

'Try as he might he can see nothing in the darkness, and the thick fog still swirls around him. There is not a sound, and there seems to be nothing he can do. There's nowhere he can run to for help, and not even the most powerful lantern would have any effect in the blanket of fog. Daniel paced up and down that path all night in a miserable and desperate state. And the next day the lengthsman found him fast asleep in the grass, not far from where the *Sophia* still lay, tied up in the shade of the trees and the horse waiting patiently in the field.

'No trace of Lucy could be found afterwards. The towpath was searched, and policemen fished around in the cut with dragnets and hooks. All the lock-keepers further down kept a lookout in case a body should drift into view. But nothing ever turned up.'

At this point Vince paused. Mike had lain transfixed by Vince's soft voice as he had spun the tale, and in his wide-awake face his eyes were bright and staring. Then his expression changed, his face relaxed as if in his thoughts he had returned from somewhere a long way off.

'What happened to Daniel?' he asked, finding his voice again.

'He left the boats and the canal a broken man,' said Kit, 'because rumours went around that he'd murdered his wife, and made up the story. We think he went mad in the end, 'specially after what 'appened later.'

'You mean there's more?' Mike had thought that the story was finished, but Vince cleared his throat and began again.

'About a year later,' he continued, 'Old Bill was passing that same stretch of the canal, on another foggy night. We call him "Old Bill",' Vince explained, 'but we don't know what his proper name was. Anyway, he had to stop and tie up, just like the Mumfords, because of the fog, even though he was an old boater and knew the road very well. But it was just too thick – couldn't see his hand in front of his face, he said.

'Old Bill had seen many things in his time on the cut, and he wasn't easily scared. But that night as he sat on the back of his boat in the fog, having a last smoke of his pipe before bed, he felt uneasy. Then he got quite a shock, because he heard in the distance behind the boat a faint voice, calling. And he knew, somehow, that it was calling to him, to Old Bill. "Help me! Heelp meeee!" said the voice.

'Old Bill put his head inside the cabin and said to his missus, "Did you hear that voice, crying out?" But his wife hadn't heard nothing. "Sounds like a lass in trouble," he said. "I'm going to have a wander down the path and see what's what." "You be careful now," said his wife. "It's pitch black, and the fog's like a soup. Don't you go falling in the water, I won't be able to help you." "I'll be all right," Bill says, chuckling, and then sets off along the towpath, picking his way very, very carefully.

'After walking for a few minutes in the gloom, and seeing and hearing nothing, he was suddenly frozen to the spot as the voice came again, this time as close as if someone were right beside him, whispering into his ear. He thought he could feel chilly lips actually brushing his ear, and the hair of his sideburns bristled.

"Help me! Heeeelp meeee!" wailed the voice, and then died away again.'

Vince was very good at doing the spooky voice, thought Mike. Too good in fact, because it was really making his flesh creep. He snuggled deeper into his bedding.

'At that moment the fog seemed to clear a little in front of him,' Vince went on, 'and far away across the canal he could make out the dim shadows of the trees on the other side. But as he looked, in the middle of the canal the mists began to swirl, and a formless mass rose up out of the water. As it grew it began to take on human shape, glowing pale white in the swirling fog. It looked like a young woman, but her form and features were shrouded. Though it made no movement, the eerie figure seemed to beckon him; and when the voice came again – more distant this time – crying "Help me!" Old Bill, though he was horror-struck, felt an urge to throw himself into the water and make for the spectre. But he resisted with all his strength; he reached out his right hand and grabbed a tree branch beside the towpath and clung to it hard until he managed to take his eyes off the hideous vision in front of him.

'When he'd pulled himself together he simply turned and fled, with the voice calling and calling behind him. Bill took no notice and just kept running. Soon he could make out the shape of his boat beside the path as he ran towards it, and he thought his ordeal was over. But just as he reached the stern and was preparing to leap aboard he was suddenly overtaken by a great black shadow which rushed past him. Like a huge terrified animal, he said it was. It made no noise, but he had a ringing in his ears after, as if someone had hit him around the head. As he recovered from the shock he could just make out the sound of feet thundering away down the path, dying away into the distance.

'He picked himself up, and with a shrug of relief he stepped aboard his boat calling to his wife. But there was no reply. The doors in the hatches were open, and he quickly jumped down inside, but the cabin was empty. Search as he might around and about he could not find her. But two days later, in the early morning, the lock-keeper several miles down the cut found her body floating near his lock gates. The face of the corpse was contorted and frozen in the most hideous look of terror anyone had ever seen, and the eyes . . .'

'That'll do, thanks!' said Kit, suddenly. 'It's a great story, Vince, but I think we all wanna sleep tonight.'

'Is there any more, then?' asked Mike, though he hoped it was the end.

'Not much,' said Vince, who had picked up the alarm clock and was winding it. 'Folks never tie up in that pound now, and even in the daytime people have seen mysterious shadows flitting between the trees, or figures apparently moving across the water. But I think our Kit's right. Time's getting on, and we don't want you having nightmares!'

'It's too late to think about that now!' laughed Mike, and the others were glad to laugh too, breaking the spell the story had woven around them. Kit always found the tale of Lucy Mumford very scary, though he had heard it many times. And Vince – though he might not admit it – often scared himself just by telling it, getting cold shivers and goose pimples at his own words. Mike glanced at the cabin doors and was relieved to see that they were still firmly shut and the slide drawn over against the rain. If it had been left open as on the previous, warmer night he might have worried a little about – well, about 'Things That go Bump in the Night!'

'Wake me up when you get up tomorrow,' whispered Mike, after Vince had set the clock and the light had been switched off. 'I want to do a full day's work, just like you.'

The heavy drumming of the rain had eased during Vince's story-telling. Now it was just a steady patter on the cabin roof. It had been a long and tiring day and – far from keeping the boys awake – the soft, regular sound soon sent them all to sleep.

12. Stuck on the Mud

It was still drizzling with rain when Kit shook his friend to wake him the next morning at a quarter to six. Mike's arms and legs felt very heavy as he rose and dressed in a drowsy blur. But as he moved about the stiffness wore off and his body slowly came to life. Though he was still only half-awake he was sensible enough to pull on a thick sweater, for the weather had turned much colder. Vince was already up and from noises in the next compartment Mike guessed that he was helping his dad to prepare the engine. From the hatches of the butty the smell of frying bacon wafted into the cabin of *Cepheus*. As it always did at home the aroma soon revived Mike, who now realised that the empty feeling in his stomach was simply hunger. Susannah was helping her mother and she passed the boys plates piled with sausage, bacon and egg. They returned to the cabin of the motor to eat it, along with large steaming mugs of tea. Kit poured four spoonfuls of sugar into his tea and Mike added three to his. 'It'll keep our strength up,' Kit said to his mum when, as she did every day, she scolded him for the amount he tipped into his cup. 'Your teeth will rot,' was Vince's only comment as he joined them to eat his breakfast.

The boats were untied and away by half past six and in the puddle-strewn streets beside the cut nothing stirred. At one bridge a green double-decker bus passed overhead. Along its side a broad colourful poster advertised 'Happy Holidays at Butlins', and pictured smiling families in beachwear beneath a blazing sun. But the windows of the bus were filled with the glum faces of silent men and women, on their way to begin work at the factories and shops. Mike heard the rattle of bottles and turned in time to see a milk float appear and disappear in the gaps between the buildings alongside the canal.

Mr Coleman was not particularly happy this morning. Another pair of boats had passed them very early and until they should meet another pair coming in the opposite direction it meant that all the locks would be set against them – a 'bad road'.

Nobody felt particularly jolly this morning, anyway. It was a dismal day – cold, wet and windy. The surface of the cut was slate grey and matched the colour of the rain-laden sky. Lock-sides were muddy and pools of water lay in the worn and broken paving around the balance beams. The boys trod carefully on the slippery stones as they worked the locks, and found it awkward turning their irons whilst wrapped up in raincoats. As the rain persisted both Mike and Kit got damper and damper till they were thoroughly wet, as the fine rain even soaked through their macs.

'We'll light the fire in our cabin later on,' Kit said, trying to cheer up Mike, who had gone very quiet. 'That'll soon dry out our clothes – and us.'

Their work was made a little easier by the crew going ahead of them who were closing gates behind them as they left each lock, and drawing paddles. So the locks were emptying when Kit and Mike reached them. Even so, it was slow work.

When at last the looked-for pair of boats appeared, travelling in the opposite direction, they were met in the worst possible place, just as *Cepheus* turned into a sharp bend in the canal. Round the blind corner the fore-end of the oncoming boat suddenly loomed up out of the grey drizzle. Mr Coleman had to steer sharply over to the right to avoid hitting the other motor. As he did so, *Cepheus* gave a lurch and tipped sideways alarmingly before coming to a sudden halt. Mike and Kit were standing on the gunwales and had to hold on tight to the cabin roof as the boat slewed to a standstill. Behind them Vince was forced to steer onto the shallows near the bank too, or the butty would have kept running ahead, straight into the back of the motor.

'We've gone aground,' said Kit, announcing the obvious to everyone. But Mike's attention was focused more on the confrontation going on between Kit's dad and the steerer of the other motor boat as he drew level. Angry words were flying, and the language was colourful – swear words that Mike had never heard before. A similar exchange occurred as the butty passed them, though it was less heated. By that time Mr Coleman was more concerned about getting the boats off the mud; it didn't matter any longer whose fault it was that they were there.

'You steer, Kit, and rev the engine when I tell you,' Mr Coleman instructed his son. Then climbing onto the cabin roof, he made his way along the top planks to the fore-end and drew a long pole out from beneath the boat's covers – the long shaft. With this he tried to push *Cepheus* off from the side of the canal.

'Throw the tiller over, Kit, and give her a good rev in reverse!' he shouted back down the boat. Mike heard the engine roar, and the water beneath the boat bubbled violently as if it were boiling. Up front Mr Coleman leaned heavily on his pole, but despite all their efforts the craft remained fast on the mud.

The rain continued its steady downpour and the whole world seemed soggy and heavy with the wet. Even the trees at the edge of the canal drooped under the weight of the water. There was no sign of life along the edge of the canal; no buildings were visible in the dim haze that surrounded them on all sides.

'What happens now?' Mike asked his friend, as Kit wound the gear wheel into neutral and Mr Coleman rested from his efforts.

'We'll 'ave to get someone to pull us off – but we could be waitin' a long time.'

Mike could see that working on the cut was not all plain sailing, pretty countryside and sunshine. He was beginning to feel a bit dejected, and began to think how at home he would be looking at the rain through a window, from the comfort of a warm room. But he was determined not to give in, and he tried to put such thoughts out of his head. 'If I'm going to be one of the boaters,' he told himself, 'then I'll have to learn to cope with problems just as they do. It's all part of being a real boater, and if Kit and his family are not complaining, then I won't either.' Nevertheless, he felt a bit helpless in this situation. Then, as a miserable gloom began to descend on the boat and its crew, he suddenly had an idea.

'Shall I make us some tea?' Mike asked, as Mr Coleman came back along the top planks to where the two boys stood on the counter.

'Good on yer, young Mike!' said Mr Coleman, and his angry and weary expression disappeared. 'Let's cool our tempers down a bit by 'aving a break, and warm up our insides with a good cuppa!' The three of them smiled at each other, and they waved to Vince and his mum who were staring at them anxiously from the stern of *Andromeda*. Susannah had stayed inside, out of the wet.

'Can't shift it!' shouted Mr Coleman to his wife and son. 'We're gonna have a brew an' wait for someone to give us a snatch!' The others replied by making thumbs-up signs and disappearing below.

In the cabin of *Cepheus* Mike already had the kettle on the primus stove and was getting mugs ready.

'Welcome to life on the cut, Mikey,' said Mr Coleman cheerfully as he entered the cabin. 'Don't worry though. It's not serious. These things often happen. It just means that we get delayed, and that gets me upset. Don't worry too much about the slangin' match I 'ad with the other boat – we all shout at each other when something goes wrong like today. Next time we pass them boats, everythin'll be sweet, just like this 'ad never 'appened. We all knows each other, and we all shouts a bit when things go wrong; but we can't fall out – they might need our help one day.'

Whilst the boats were stopped Kit lit a fire in the stove. Beginning with some old oily rags and kindling wood he soon had a good blaze going. To this he added lumps of shiny black coal from the box behind the cabin step. Within twenty minutes there was a bright red glow from the ventilator holes in the cast-iron door and the little stove began to throw out plenty of heat. Through the open doors the boys could see the thick yellow-grey smoke from the newly-lit fire billowing around the stern of the boat in the wind, before swirling away down the cut. There was an acrid smell from the wisps that drifted in through the doors.

'Whatever else happens to us,' said Kit, relaxing from his efforts as he sat back on the side-bed next to Mike to enjoy the warmth, 'we never goes cold!'

Then he explained to Mike how all the boaters, if they were carrying a load of coal, always topped up their little bunkers with some of the fuel, for their own use. It wasn't really stealing, he said, because the amounts were so small they were never missed. 'What are a few pounds compared with fifty tons?' he said. It was one of the 'perks of the job'.

'Sometimes we swap a bit of coal for some eggs or vegetables at one of the lock-keepers' cottages,' said Kit. 'People's always happy to take coal instead of money.'

Having finished his tea, Mr Coleman went on lookout for passing boats. Eventually, after they had been waiting there for about forty-five minutes, the boats still at a forlorn angle on the mud, a pair appeared coming along the canal behind them. Mr Coleman shouted to them as soon as they were near enough to hear.

'We're stemmed-up,' he cried (meaning they were stuck). 'What about giving us a snatch?'

The crew of the passing boats obliged with hardly a word and without appearing even to slow down much. Ropes were thrown and attached and soon *Cepheus* was dragged from its muddy perch in the shallows. As it came free the ropes were loosed and tossed back and Kit revved the engine to take the boat clear of the obstruction. A few more minutes and *Andromeda* was drawn free of the mud too, and they were on their way once more.

As the morning wore on the rain stopped. Before eleven o'clock a pale sun began to break through small gaps in the dull grey mass above. By midday only small puffs of cloud remained in a bright blue sky and the hot summer sun blazed down on them all once again. But the air was still fresh after the rain and the occasional gusts of wind were chilly. All about them the countryside smelled very rich, and a feast of scents wafted over the water to them. Mike and Kit had hung their wet things on the rail above the cabin stove to dry before hopping onto the butty boat where they made thick corned-beef and pickle sandwiches for everyone. The main task now was to make up for the lost time. But the boats that had rescued them were in front, and progress at locks was slow.

13. Into the Tunnel

Since the previous day all the locks had been uphill, steadily raising the canal higher and higher. By late afternoon it was heading towards a broad hillside, which it approached in a steep-sided cutting. The two boys were on the butty when Kit called out to Mike, who followed his friend as he ran along the top-planks to the fore-end of *Andromeda*.

'There's the first tunnel!' Kit said excitedly, pulling at Mike's sleeve and pointing with his other hand. 'Remember, I told you about it yesterday?'

To one side of *Cepheus*, which lay across their view ahead, Mike could see how the canal appeared to come to an end below a high wooded bank. Then, peering into the distance, he could see the dark tunnel entrance – a low arched hole over the water, set in a broad brick buttress with the hill towering above. He thought the opening very small and began to wonder how the boats would fit inside.

'We'd better get back to the cabin,' Kit said. 'We'll 'ave to stand by me mum at the elum, otherwise it's a bit dangerous. But you'll be able to see all right.'

The boats drew closer to the tunnel mouth and Mike realised that it wasn't quite so small as it had first appeared. But it was still going to be a tight fit, he thought. Ahead of them *Cepheus* slowed down, and as *Andromeda* slowly caught up, Vince, who was on the motor with his dad, began to take in some of the long line. When the boats entered the tunnel shortly after, the butty was tied closer to *Cepheus* and followed directly in the wake of the motor.

From the hatches of the butty Mike had a good view of the tunnel entrance. Its red brick sides were worn with age and the passage of many boats. It looked very ancient, like the gateway to a mythical underground kingdom. It looked very dark inside, very dark indeed, and not at all welcoming. *Cepheus* disappeared into the darkness first and then the tunnel gradually swallowed up the length of *Andromeda*. Mike felt he wanted to duck as he passed the gaping tunnel mouth, it seemed so low. Then they were inside and the first thing that Mike noticed was the sheer blackness of this narrow brick tube; and in the blackness, the racket from the engine on *Cepheus*. Even though it was some yards ahead of them its steady chug-chug-chug echoed noisily off the walls. As his eyes became accustomed to the gloom Mike could see the bricks on the tunnel sides, still illuminated by the last fragments of sunlight straying in from the entrance behind. Within a few moments, however, the light faded and it was difficult to see anything at all.

Ahead of them a pale yellow arc of light circled round the tunnel roof. This, Mrs Coleman said, was from the electric headlight on the fore-end of *Andromeda*, and beyond it another paler arc could be seen deeper in the gloom – the headlight of the motor. The boats carried lights so that they could see to navigate at night and be seen by other craft approaching. Here the beam lit up the tunnel a little and so helped the steerer to position the boat in the narrow space. There seemed to be very little room on each side of the boat and Mike kept his hands well inside the safety of the hatches; he didn't want to graze himself on the passing bricks. He stood to the left of Mrs Coleman, who was steering, and Kit stood on her right. Susannah was down inside the cabin – she thought the tunnel a spooky place and was a little afraid of its chilly darkness.

Mike soon noticed how cold the tunnel was, especially since the heat of the sun had been full on his back only moments before. He turned round and saw behind him the bright disc of the tunnel mouth – a semicircle of retreating daylight with its broken reflection in the water. It reminded Mike of looking down a long tube of cardboard.

'Mind you don't get a shower, Mike,' Kit warned. 'Some bits of the roof are wet and drippy – and you can't tell when they're comin' up!' Then Kit cried out, because they had at that very moment passed beneath a trickle of water falling steadily from the darkness overhead. 'It got me!' he shouted. 'And me!' said Mike as the freezing drops ran down the back of his neck too. 'It's a bit like going on the ghost train at the fair!' he giggled. 'This is really good fun!' The cold shower had livened him up and he was really alert and quite jumpy – he didn't want to get another soaking, but there was no way of telling when the next shower might come.

Mrs Coleman laughed at them both. She had put on her headscarf as they went into the tunnel, and besides, she had travelled through tunnels countless times before and they held no mystery or surprises for her. 'You're not made of sugar,' she said to the boys. 'A bit of water won't do you no harm!'

Mike had travelled through railway tunnels and remembered how they were passed very swiftly, often in a few moments, because of the speed of the train. Enclosed in the safety of a well-lit carriage you hardly noticed the tunnel at all. But when the usual speed was about four miles per hour on the boats he could see it was going to be a long time before they would see daylight again.

'How long's this tunnel?' he asked.

'About a mile and six furlongs,' said Kit.

'Crikey!' Mike exclaimed. 'That means it'll take . . .' and there was a pause while he wrestled with the figures to work out their journey time through the hillside.

'It takes about forty minutes.' Mrs Coleman came to his rescue – sums had never been Mike's strong subject and he was glad to be spared this little mental arithmetic puzzle.

'Forty minutes!' Mike said to himself. That was nearly half a football match – and all spent in this noisy, dank hole! Another thought occurred to him and he shared it with the others.

'How on earth did they get the boats through these tunnels before they had engines,' he asked. 'The horses couldn't pull them through, could they?'

'They were legged through,' Kit replied.

'Legged?' said Mike, sensing he was about to learn another canal word.

'Yeah,' Kit said. 'It wasn't much of a job. They put long planks across the boats and two fellas – the leggers – had to lay on their backs on the planks, one each side. Then they sort of walked along the tunnel walls, so that the boats moved along with them. It took ages.'

'There were tugs too, don't forget, Kit,' his mother reminded him. 'Some of the tunnels had steam or electric tug-boats, which pulled boats through, several at a time in a long train. But it's much simpler now that we have the motor boats.'

'How did the horses get through?' asked Mike, who was still struggling to imagine the leggers at their task. He half-expected to be told that the horses were put into special little boats, tied to the craft that they usually pulled.

'The 'orses were led over the top of the tunnel, Mike, along the 'orse path,' said Mrs Coleman. 'Usually one of the children did that, and they'd meet the boats again at the other end.'

The uneven walls of the old tunnel passed slowly on either side of the boat, faintly illuminated by a dim glow from the cabin light. After about ten minutes travelling through the clammy, dank darkness Mike detected an eerie pale glow hovering above the boats some distance ahead. It gave him a bit of a fright when he noticed it.

'What's that?' he cried, feeling just a little bit uneasy. 'There's a sort of misty light in front – looks like a ghost!'

'Wooooooooh!' wailed Kit, in his best spooky voice, and the tunnel reverberated with his cry. 'It's the ghost of old Mick Murphy, the navvy, who died digging the tunnel. Woooooooooh!'

'Stop it Kit, that's not funny,' said Mrs Coleman. 'Sorry,' Kit replied. 'I was only tryin' to frighten Mike, for a laugh.' But even as Kit apologised, an echoing wail could be heard from the depths of the tunnel ahead.

'That'll be our Vince,' said Kit. 'He thinks we're trying to scare him, and now he's trying to frighten us.'

'I was scared already,' said Mike, 'but I know it isn't a ghost; only, I don't know *what* it is. I can't make it out at all.'

'You'll see soon enough, Mike,' said Mrs Coleman, 'but I didn't want our Kit to make fun of the dead. When these tunnels was dug through the hill it was all done by candlelight, by men with picks and shovels. It was 'ard work, and can't have been very pleasant. In some tunnels they used gunpowder, to blast their way through the rocky bits, and many poor men lost their lives in these 'orrible places. I wouldn't blame them if they *did* come back to haunt us, but it isn't fair to make fun of them.'

'I am sorry Mum, honest! You know I didn't mean it,' Kit said again, and he sounded really crestfallen.

'I know, love,' replied Mrs Coleman, in a gentler tone of voice, 'but just think before you say such things next time.'

By now the eerie glow, which looked like a spaceship coming in to land, was only a few yards ahead of them. They could see it sweeping across the top of *Cepheus* like a searchlight, illuminating first the top-planks and then the cabin with an icy-cold light. Vince, who was steering, suddenly appeared clearly before their eyes as if caught in the flashlight of a camera, and then instantly vanished into the velvety blackness. Now the great cylinder of light was coming along the top-planks of *Andromeda*, bathing everything in its monochrome, greyish pallor until it swept over the heads of the three figures on the stern of the butty. As he was caught momentarily in the brightness of the beam Mike looked up and saw a long cylindrical shaft soaring up to the open air. High up above him, as if he were looking up from the bottom of a deep well, he had a brief glimpse of the sky and clouds and then the impenetrable darkness of the tunnel enveloped everything once more. Mike turned, blinking his dazzled eyes, and behind the boat watched the receding shaft of light shining down upon the agitated water. It looked just like a spotlight on an empty stage.

'It's a ventilation shaft,' explained Kit to his friend, who'd realised that it was nothing to be scared of. 'There's a few of 'em in this tunnel,' Kit went on. 'It was down them that the men first dug, to start the proper tunnel below; but afterwards they left them there to let all the fumes get out.'

Even so, the tunnel was still very smelly. The exhaust from the diesel engines and smoke from the cabin fire seemed to hang about in the damp atmosphere, burning Mike's throat and making him cough.

The fleeting glimpse of the sunny sky up above had emphasised the gloom of the tunnel through which Mike and the boats were moving, deep beneath the hillside. The dense blackness, and the drumming of the engine, and the choking fumes suggested to him a journey into some infernal region of goblins and dwarfs – even into hell itself (though he admitted that hell might have been a bit hotter). Worse still, the entrance far behind them was now just a distant speck of light and the darkness that closed in behind *Andromeda* looked thick enough to cut. With Vince's ghostly bedtime tale still fresh in his mind Mike couldn't stop himself looking anxiously over his shoulder now and again. He had the weird feeling that some unknown thing was there, in the darkness, close by. He was glad of the glow from the cabin light below him and the happy, carefree chatter from those around him. 'How dreadful to fall off the boat,' he thought, 'and be left behind in this lonely and dismal drain. I hope I don't end up having nightmares about this.'

In the featureless gloom it was difficult to tell how long they had been travelling, but the next thing that Mike noticed was the sound of another engine up ahead. Kit's mother said, 'There's a pair of boats coming, we're going to pass in the tunnel.'

Again Mike looked over the side of the boat where there seemed only inches between him and the rough tunnel wall. 'It's all right,' Mrs Coleman said, as if she understood Mike's anxiety. 'There's plenty of room!'

A bright light was visible ahead, only this time it was very clearly electric. It reminded Mike of driving at night along a dark country road with his mum and dad, when the headlights of an approaching car would dazzle his dad at the wheel.

The light hung there in the distance for what seemed an eternity. It didn't appear to get any closer until suddenly it was right beside them, passing down the side of *Cepheus* and *Andromeda*. Despite the narrowness of the tunnel the boats passed without touching. Mike heard the throbbing engine of the motor boat as its engine hole slid past. Then for a brief moment he saw the silhouette of the steerer at his tiller, the man touching the peak of his flat cap as he greeted Mrs Coleman. Behind him the dark shape of the butty glided by, its steerer just a shadowy figure crouched in the hatches. The engine noise faded to a distant echo as the boats were swallowed up in the darkness.

The excitement of this encounter was barely over when they passed another ventilation shaft, gaping overhead – only this one had a stream running down its sides. A cascade of icy-cold water, pouring off the rim of the shaft, showered Mike from head to foot as he passed underneath. His body stiffened as freezing rivulets ran down his back and his agonised cry echoed round the tunnel walls. Mrs Coleman suggested that he go inside, before he got any wetter. Kit – for whom tunnels were no novelty anyway – went inside with him. They were talking and laughing together when, twenty minutes later, the boats emerged from the end of the tunnel and bright sunlight streamed in through the doors of the cabin. Kit and Mike rushed out into the hatches and saw the brick portal of the northern end of the tunnel. In the daylight it looked harmless and not at all threatening, and the boys thought no more about ghosts or of the dark, echoing, underhill world they had just passed through. Instead they climbed onto the cabin roof and lay there, gazing up at the clear blue sky, whilst the heat of the late afternoon dried their hair and damp clothing.

14. Sister Molly

The Colemans were up bright and early as usual the next morning, and a mist lay across the fields, promising a hot day ahead. Within a few hours the boats reached a series of locks at the top of which stood a small village, where houses and a pub lay close beside the canal. This little village seemed to have been made for the canal, which ran through it like a main street. The front doors of its cottages opened straight onto the lock-side, and the ancient pub – with a thatched roof so low that it brushed men's hats as they walked past – also looked onto the water. On each side of its door there was an ancient grey settle, on which old men would sit to savour their beer and watch the boats going past.

'Better go and see Sister Molly, Vincent,' Mrs Coleman said to her son as they stood talking on the butty. 'Get her to check your arm and redo the dressing.'

'It'll be all right, Mum. Don't make a fuss,' was Vince's reply.

'Oh well, please yourself. But you try getting past her eagle eye, then!' said his mother. Vince jumped off at the locks and went to work the paddles and gates with Mike. Kit had been sent ahead to top up the water cans at a tap near the pub, whilst Susannah ran off to the little village shop for her mother.

As the boats rose in the last lock right in the heart of the little village, Mike saw a curious figure emerge from one of the cottages. A heavily starched apron was tied about her middle, and a white starched nurse's headdress framed the wrinkled and pink face of this old lady, her forehead fringed with tiny curls of silver hair. After watching the Colemans approach she stepped down from her doorway and hurried to the lock-side in tiny shuffling steps.

'Oh, how lovely to see you all, my dears. I do hope you're all quite well,' she said in greeting, with her small hands clasped across the front of her apron. Her chirping voice was warm and kind, and it was evident that she was familiar with the boat people, and was herself part of the life of the cut.

'Now, what's the matter with that arm, Master Vincent?' she enquired, moving to where the lad stood waiting at the top gates. 'I think you'd better let me have a little peep!'

'It's nothin' much, Sister Molly,' Vince said. 'Only a cut I got last week. It's healed up now, anyway.' But the old lady, though tiny and frail-looking, would not be put off. She took Vince's arm firmly in her hands and inspected the bandages with which Mike's mum had bound his wound. Vince, big teenage lad that he was, submitted to the old lady's attentions without a word. She tutted a little, and shook her head. It was over a week since Vince's arm had been gashed and the dressing was now quite blackened and tattered with wear. Sister Molly quickly removed the shabby bandage and inspected the scar beneath. Vince explained how it had happened and introduced Mike, who had come to stand beside him. 'Mike's mum came to the rescue,' he said, 'and then Mike came to join us on the boats for a while.'

'She's in the Saint John's Ambulance,' said Mike, proudly.

'Well, she made a very good job of it,' said Sister Molly, with obvious approval. 'But it needs some sticking plaster now, just to protect it for a few more days. Wait there!' And she scuttled off back to her cottage.

'Sister Molly knows everybody on the cut,' said Vince, as the tiny, stooped figure disappeared through the cottage door. 'She's wonderful really. She's been lookin' after us all for years and years. We all trusts her, an' she helps with everything – coughs and colds, toothache and measles, delivering babies, getting rid of nits and fleas. Everyone comes to Sister Molly.'

As he spoke the old lady reappeared, hopping lightly from her cottage towards the lock like a little bird. Within seconds she had swabbed Vince's forearm with pungent antiseptic and dressed it with a length of sticking plaster. Patting the arm as she finished she then turned her attention to Mike. 'What a handsome young man!' she declared, and she wanted to know where he came from, how old he was, and if he was keeping well. 'No tummy trouble? Has the heat brought out any rashes?' But Mike was able to assure her that, for the moment at least, he was quite well. 'You've got lovely teeth,' remarked Sister Molly. 'You've been a good boy and looked after them very well. I wish I could say the same of all of my boating people!' she added with a sigh. Kit ran up to join them and greeted Sister Molly as if she were an old auntie or grandmother. She, in turn, was evidently delighted to see him.

'Now, I've got something else for you before you go,' said the old nurse to Kit. 'Just come to my surgery for a moment,' and she led the way with the two boys trotting along behind. Inside, the front room of the cottage smelled fresh and clean, of surgical spirit and disinfectant. There were shelves of medicines and boxes of dressings, and two charts on the wall had illustrations of the human body showing the nervous system and the skeleton. The walls were painted in creamy gloss paint that shone and caught reflections. Everywhere was spotless and neat, but at the same time it was homely – not like the doctor's surgery that Mike knew, or the clinic where he used to go with his mother to collect orange juice and tins of dried milk. Through the open window wafted the scent of honeysuckle, and roses could be seen, clustered about the door frame.

'Take this to your mother,' said Sister Molly, who had lifted down from the shelf a large glass bottle, ribbed down its back, which contained a pale pink liquid. She thrust it into Kit's hand, saying, 'It's calamine lotion, my dear. All of you have such fair skin, and in this heat you're sure to get burned. And they say it's going to get hotter still. This will soothe those red patches! So make sure you put plenty on! It has a lovely smell, and it will feel wonderfully cool. Now, you must be on your way or they'll go without you! Come along!' The old lady shooed them out of the door as if she were chasing hens; then she chuckled to herself and waved as Mike and Kit hurried towards the boats which were waiting just above the lock.

Mike had hardly settled back on board before the boats rounded a bend and another tunnel appeared ahead of them, just as Kit had predicted. Mike felt that, like Kit, he wanted to express his indifference – what was a tunnel after all? He'd been through one already, hadn't he? It was no big deal. But he found it impossible to repress the excitement he truly felt and, just as before, he stood transfixed on the stern of the butty – with Vince this time – all the way through. Again he marvelled at the incredible feat of digging a canal right through the hillside. Again he managed to get scared in the spooky darkness – without the help of Kit this time, who remained inside talking to his mum and Susannah. But at least he didn't get wet. This tunnel was dryer than the first and its main interest lay in the fact that it was not quite straight.

'The men dug from both ends,' Vince explained, 'but they didn't quite meet in the same place in the middle. That's why it's got this funny kink in it.' The boats bumped about a bit and scraped the walls as they negotiated the uneven passage, then after more than half an hour in the cool darkness they emerged into fresh air once again.

It was another day of hot sunshine. Morning turned to afternoon, and as the afternoon heat grew, so the locks began to come thick and fast until the boats reached what looked to Mike like a mountainside of locks. Huge pairs of black gates strode up the hillside ahead of them, one behind the other as far as he could see. It was a gruelling task to work the boats up these locks and everyone lent a hand. Occasionally they passed boats coming downwards and then the locks were set in their favour. As they climbed steadily up the flight Mike could see more and more of the countryside spread out behind. Below him a big town sprawled, dominated by the tall, imposing tower of a large church. And beyond, in the hazy sunshine, lay a broad expanse of outlying factories and distant fields. Now and again the sunlight shone out briefly in dazzling beams reflected from glasshouses, factory roofs or the windows of motor cars passing noiselessly across the landscape a mile or more away.

Mike concentrated hard on his work, and because there was no let-up in the succession of gates and paddles few words were exchanged between him and Kit. Instead he let his imagination take over. He began to see each lock as an enemy out-post, and himself as part of an army storming its way to the top of the hill. Soon Kit had picked up the idea and joined him in the game and together they threw themselves into the assault, one on each side of the channel. As they crouched by each heavy balance beam they were sheltering from enemy fire. Between the locks they rushed for cover across open ground, diving in and out behind bushes or bollards or old sheds standing beside the cut. Without hesitating or lingering they dashed up the steps to the next lock, tossing imaginary grenades over the tops of the gates to disable the enemy within. Each lock passed was a 'victory' over the opposing troops, and each victory led them nearer to their goal. Still, it took nearly two hours to 'conquer the enemy', and by the time they reached the top Mike was ready to drop. His body ached all over from the constant winding of paddles and pushing and pulling of the gates (which still had to be done, even in the heat of 'battle'). He could hardly catch his breath and was slouched, panting over the beam of the final gate. Even Kit – who rarely displayed any sign of fatigue – appeared weary too. As he looked across the watery divide all he could do was grin in sympathy at his shattered friend.

'I hope me mum's got us a drink ready – and something to eat,' he gasped, as he and Mike opened the last pair of gates for the boats to leave the lock and the two of them almost fell aboard the butty. He had hardly finished speaking when Mrs Coleman shouted 'Cocoa!' Though the day was hot the cocoa was very nourishing and refreshing and the boys drank their frothing mugs eagerly and quickly. Then, to their delight, a pile of jam sandwiches was presented to them too.

'You deserved that, boys,' said Mrs Coleman, 'you've worked really hard today. No more locks till tomorrow, so 'ave a good rest now. There's nothin' else to do till we tie up.'

Kit and Mike lay flat out on the cabin roof, silent for the remainder of the journey. Mike felt his face glowing. His brow had been perspiring through the heat and hard work and now the sun was catching it too. Weary from all his efforts he simply relaxed in the sunshine, closed his eyes and enjoyed the sensation of having nothing to do at all – not even to talk or think – and the closeness of his friend. Kit had rested his head on Mike's tummy, and Mike's arm was flopped across the other boy's middle. They were comfortable with each other and their growing friendship didn't need any words. Even the occasional cries of greeting from passing boaters hardly disturbed their repose; voices that seemed detached, remote, from another world.

Mike slept like a log that night. Everyone had stayed aboard in the evening, because the boats had tied up in the countryside far from any signs of life. Mike and Kit went to bed early, exhausted, and nothing – not even the chatter and laughter from the butty, which went on till very late – could prevent their heavy eyelids from closing as soon as their heads hit the pillow, nor disturb their well-earned sleep.

15. Over the Fields for Eggs

'Not far off the place where we unload now, Mike!'

The next morning Kit was telling his friend what the day would bring as they shared a basin of soapy water. In their usual frantic, if unsuccessful attempt to scrub face and limbs thoroughly, much water was distributed around the cabin and, again as usual, Vince shouted at the two of them for being so messy. As usual they took no notice, and as usual they pulled on their clothes and ran a comb roughly through their dampened hair before tackling breakfast, which fortified them for the day's work.

'There might be other boats there already, waitin' to unload, so we could be tied up for a long time. If we're lucky we might 'ave a chance to go to the pictures. An' there's swimming baths close by too. I'd love to go there, 'cause I really wanna learn to swim.'

'Can't you swim?' said Mike, through a mouthful of fried bread and bacon. He was surprised. He imagined that anyone living and working on the water would be really good at swimming. He was a strong swimmer himself; he had learned at school and had swum in competitions.

'Nah, not yet,' his friend replied, stirring more sugar into his already sweet tea. 'We usually tries to stay *out* of the water if possible!' and he laughed.

It was a point of honour for the boatmen never to fall overboard – and certainly never to be *seen* falling into the canal. Such clumsiness would be terribly embarrassing. So learning to swim must have seemed rather pointless. Unlike Mike and his friends at school, the children from the boats didn't often have the time to go looking for entertainment in the towns where they stopped; and when they did they preferred other things to the swimming baths. But Kit loved to be in the water and so it was arranged that – if they had time – Mike would do his best to teach his friend to swim.

The boats had set off early and were making good progress. There would be no locks for a couple of hours, so the boys whiled away the time on the fore-end of the motor, taking it easy after their hard work of the previous day. Kit dug out some lengths of old rope from the store of odds and ends in the deck locker and eagerly began to show Mike how to splice the ends together.

'Me dad taught me this,' he said, 'and me Uncle Alf – that's the one our Joyce lives with – he showed me how to do it as well. Ropes cost money, and they do get snapped now and then. So it's a good idea to know how to join them up again.'

Mike watched carefully as Kit dextrously wove the coarse strands together, drawing the plaits really tight and poking in the remaining ends so that the joint looked neat and tidy.

'You 'ave a go now!' he said, and rummaged to find two more discarded lengths. Kit guided Mike's fingers as he struggled to copy what he had watched his friend do so easily. Eventually Mike succeeded in joining the two ends – though his efforts looked more like a tangled ball of string such as his dad kept in a drawer in the kitchen. Kit looked at it sceptically and tried unsuccessfully to stifle his giggles. Then he said that they should test Mike's handiwork. This they did by pulling the joined lengths like a Christmas cracker. Unfortunately the two halves separated rather like a Christmas cracker too, only there was no snap and no novelty inside. Mike looked and felt rather disappointed.

'It's a skill, Mike,' his friend said, reassuringly. 'It takes time. You just need a bit more practice, tha's all. I'm not brilliant at it,' he went on, modestly, 'an' I've been doing it for ages.' Then he added, 'But if it was a matter of life and death, I still don't think I'd trust a rope that had been spliced by me!' And the two of them laughed as they imagined swinging across the cut like Tarzan, on one of Kit's spliced ropes, only to get a ducking as it parted halfway across.

Around midday Mrs Coleman fried omelettes for their dinner. She filled them with rich red cheese, tasty pink chopped Spam, and mushrooms picked from the fields early that morning. Everyone had a thick slice and the boys smothered theirs in dollops of ketchup. There were chunks of crusty bread too and bananas afterwards.

The boats ploughed onwards during meals – they couldn't be delayed by stopping to eat. So Kit took his dad's dinner along to him on the motor. The plateful of omelette was covered with a second plate to keep it warm, and then – plates carefully balanced – Kit jumped off the butty at a convenient place where two bridges stood close together. From the first bridge-hole he ran like mad along the towpath to get ahead of the boats. Then he handed the plate to his father at the next bridge-hole, before stepping back onto the butty again as it passed. Mr Coleman placed the meal in front of him on the cabin slide and ate as he steered the boat.

Not only did the boats not stop for meals, but shopping too had to be done without holding up the journey. There weren't many little shops like the one at the Wharf Inn, and often a quick trip had to be made into a village or town whilst the boats were loading, unloading or working through the locks. Along their route the boatmen's wives got to know where lock-keepers were willing to sell vegetables from their gardens, or farms that would supply them with foodstuffs too. Now Mrs Coleman had used up all her eggs in the omelettes because she knew that there would be a chance to replenish her store that afternoon.

'Susie!' Mrs Coleman called to her daughter. 'Why don't you take Mikey and run up to the farm for some eggs – and see what else Mrs Baker might have as well. I'll give you some money.'

'Okay Mum.' Susannah put down the book she'd been trying to read and climbed out of the cabin of the butty. She shouted to Mike who was sitting on the fore-end of *Andromeda* talking to Kit.

'Jump off at the bridge 'ole, Mike. We're goin' to the farm!'

There was a bridge within a hundred yards and Susannah got ready to jump from the back of the butty whilst Mike prepared to leap from the front. He was much more sure-footed now and quite used to leaving and joining the boats in this way. Once on the bank Susannah led Mike over a stile and together they half-ran, half-walked up a very overgrown path towards a cluster of sheds and rooftops just visible over the brow of the hill.

'We're going to Baker's farm,' said Susannah. 'We often stop off here to get a few things. I like coming up here because I can see the horses.'

And sure enough there, halfway up the hill, Mike could see several brown and black horses gathered at a gate beside the path. They were fine-looking animals; hunters put out to grass for the summer months. Their heads were hung over the top of the gate as if they had anticipated Susannah's arrival.

'I wish I could have a horse,' she confided to Mike. 'They're such lovely creatures, so beautiful. And I think they need someone to really love them, which I would.' Mike rarely saw horses in the town where he lived, though he knew that Amanda James belonged to a pony club. He saw her every Saturday dressed in jodhpurs and a black riding hat as her dad took her off in the car. He'd always thought that riding was a girly thing, but seeing these handsome creatures in the wide-open countryside he thought how impressive they were. Apart from anything else they were really graceful, but he marvelled at how big and powerful they looked too. He felt a little afraid of them at close quarters and didn't stand too near their nodding heads; but he couldn't help thinking how exciting it would be to climb up on one of those broad backs and canter off across the fields.

'We didn't bring anythin' to give them,' Susannah said sadly. 'I should 'ave asked me mum for some carrots or some sugar.' Instead she stooped and picked a large handful of the longest and greenest grass she could find and, approaching the gate, fed it to a glossy black horse which tossed its head and wriggled with excitement on seeing her. 'I wonder what its name is,' said Susannah. 'It looks just like the picture of Black Beauty in my book.'

'Looks like Champion the Wonder Horse,' said Mike, who had never read *Black Beauty*, but knew the TV adventures of the horse called Champion.

'I'll call him Jet,' said Susannah, 'because he's jet black – and because I bet he can go really fast like a jet rocket.'

Mike grabbed a tuft of grass too, and, plucking up courage, offered it to a second horse. The warmth of its breath on his hand surprised him. 'Feed him with your palm held flat, Mike,' Susannah advised, 'then he won't eat your hand as well.'

'I think this one can be called Conker,' Mike replied, 'because he's shiny and brown like a chestnut – and I bet he could "conquer" all the other horses in a race!'

Susannah laughed. 'You are funny, Mike,' she said. 'Can't hang around though, or we'll keep the boats waiting,' and she suddenly turned on her heel and escorted Mike briskly up the path toward the farmyard.

'I wish we had a horse-boat, like the ones from the olden days,' she went on. 'Then I could be the one who looked after the horse, and I'd feed 'im and groom 'im every day, and look after his harnesses and everything.'

Whilst Susannah was still enjoying her little dream she and Mike arrived at the muddy, straw-strewn yard amidst an assortment of barns and sheds. Some of these were quite modern and their painted corrugated sheeting glowed bright red in the sunlight. There were strong smells in the air, of animal feed, and straw, and manure and diesel fuel. Parked nearby were a brand new green tractor and a battered Land Rover with a trailer full of bales on the back. They could hear activity in one of the sheds, so they approached the door and peeped in. Inside was a burly man in wellingtons and a cap distributing clean straw around pens that contained dozens of black and white pigs, squealing and running excitedly in all directions.

'Hello Mr Baker!' called Susannah.

'Oh, hello lass!' the man replied, turning to show his reddened but friendly face. 'Come for some eggs have you? The missus is in the house I think, or she might be in the chicken runs – go and have a look, anyway.'

'Come on!' Susannah said to Mike, and she hurried across the yard and round a corner to where a little wooden gate led into a small garden behind the farmhouse. Bright white sheets billowed on the line, straining to free themselves from their pegs in the strong breeze. The children knocked at the back door, which was slightly ajar, and it opened almost immediately as Mrs Baker appeared, drying her hands on a large towel.

'You're lucky,' she said, obviously recognising Susannah straight away. 'I've just this minute come in. And if you've come for eggs, my love, then I've lots and lots of gorgeous brown ones that I've picked from under the hens not five minutes ago.'

Though she was very cheerful, Mrs Baker was not Mike's idea of a farmer's wife – the sort he had read about in storybooks. She was very tall and thin and wore a very smart bottle-green velvet skirt and jacket, and stout brown brogues that creaked slightly as she walked. Her hair was quite short and grey, and she wore a strand of pearls about her neck. She also spoke in very refined tones, and if he had seen her anywhere else Mike would have thought she was a librarian or a schoolteacher. But he didn't have much time to ponder all this, because as soon as Mrs Baker had fetched two boxes of eggs, and a few coins had changed hands,

Susannah said, 'Come on Mike, best get back to the boats, quick!'

'Would your mother like some honey, do you think?' said Mrs Baker, stopping the children in their tracks.

'Oooh yes! I should think so,' Susannah replied.

'The bees have been very productive this summer,' continued the farmer's wife, 'and we've simply jars and jars. Take some for the family.'

'I haven't got much money left,' Susannah said, searching in her pocket. 'I've only sixpence,' and she held the single silver coin aloft as proof.

'That's quite all right, my dear – it's sixpence a jar anyway!' said Mrs Baker brightly, disappearing into her kitchen. She emerged a minute later with a large jar of the golden honey and slipped it into a brown paper bag.

'Take care on your way back – you'll look after her, won't you, young man?' This last remark was addressed to Mike, whom till now she seemed not to have noticed at all. The children turned to leave once more, but Mrs Baker spoke up again.

'Wait, wait!' she said. 'There's one more thing,' and she fled through the door before they had a chance to say a word. When she returned she quickly thrust another brown paper bag into Mike's hands, then shooed them away. 'That's for your tea, my dears, and now hurry home; off you go!'

The children thanked Mrs Baker several times over, waving to her in her doorway as Susannah led the way out of the yard. They took a different path home, one that bordered a field of ripe barley and curved away from the farm to a point further along the cut.

As they hurried over a ridge in the hillside they could see below them the long hedgerow which marked the line of the canal. Above it the blue and yellow cabin sides of *Cepheus* and *Andromeda* were clearly visible, moving slowly along in the sunlight.

'They're still a little way off the next lock,' Susannah said. 'We'll get there in plenty of time, no need to hurry now,' and she slackened her pace a little. Beside them the barley rippled like water as a strong summer breeze bent the tufted heads of grain. Gust after gust sent broad waves chasing across the field. A pair of rabbits bobbed out from beneath the hedgerow, pausing momentarily with heads and ears erect when they saw the children. Then they turned, bounded down the headland and disappeared into the thick corn where invisible skylarks trilled their florid song.

'What's in the bag?' Susannah asked, and Mike carefully opened the brown paper package to peep inside. Wrapped in greaseproof paper were two large slices of a very dark and moist-looking cake with thick icing. 'Coooo! It's chocolate cake,' he said, and a rich aroma wafted up from the open wrapping. 'Mmmm, my favourite!'

'I could eat it now,' said Susannah, and Mike agreed – his mouth was watering already. But they resisted the temptation and carefully re-wrapped the delicious treat for later.

'I'm sure this honey costs more than a tanner,' Susannah said to Mike.

'Yeah, more like a shilling I should think, or even one-and-six,' Mike replied. He'd been thinking that the farmer's wife was very generous.

'She's always so kind to us, that Mrs Baker. One day she showed us round the milking parlour. It was really interestin', and noisy with all the machines – the special pumps that collect the milk and all that. The cows were really quiet, though. It didn't seem to bother them at all. And afterwards she gave us some lovely butter, I've never tasted anything like it. She *gave* it to us, and wouldn't let us pay nothing.'

'Were you with your Mum then?' asked Mike.

'No, it was me an' our Joyce – it was when I was very small.'

'I expect she just loves children,' Mike went on. 'Sometimes people have only to see children and they go all gooey and make a fuss of them and give them presents.' He was thinking of one or two of his aunts and his mum's friends. They were nice people, but he didn't like being made a fuss of and was embarrassed if they brought him things when it wasn't even his birthday.

'How long is it since Joyce went to work with your uncle and auntie?' he asked, interested to know more about this older sister.

''Bout two years ago,' said Susannah. 'I was sorry when she went. We still see her, now and then, but I miss having her around. We were really good friends, and now I haven't anyone to talk to. Not in the way that we used to talk; you know, sharing secrets and things.'

Mike, who didn't have a brother but had often imagined what it would be like if he did, felt he knew exactly what she meant. He'd noticed what good friends Kit and Vince seemed to be, as well as brothers. As Mike trudged along with Susannah by his side he thought of Kit, and how great it would be to have a brother of his own, just like him.

16. Brummagem

'That Mrs Baker spoils you children,' said Mrs Coleman, when Susannah and Mike rejoined her on *Andromeda*. 'And you must take her some more money for the honey next time you go up. It's very good of her to give us things cheaply, but I like to pay my way, I do,' she said proudly.

'Money for the honey; Money for the honey!' sang Susannah, who had picked up her mother's unintentional rhyme and was now trying to turn it into a song. The boats were rising in the lock by this time and Mrs Coleman, despairing of her daughter, said, 'Oh, go an' help the boys!' So Susannah climbed onto the cabin roof, waited till the boat reached the level of the lock side, then skipped off.

Mike had already gone to join Kit on the lock. Vince, who had been operating paddles and opening and shutting gates with Kit whilst the others were at the farm, went back to the butty to let his mother carry on with her cooking. Once on the bank Susannah ran about in the grass, still singing her little song, and then went searching in the hedgerows for blackberries, but got distracted by some butterflies and chased those instead.

Whilst they were waiting for the lock to fill Kit and Mike lay on the long balance beams of the lock gates. The beams were deeply furrowed where the timber had begun to open up with age. Sometimes small plants could be found growing in these cracks, or tiny insects might be seen scurrying in and out of holes. Because they were painted black the old beams absorbed the sun's heat and were very warm and comfortable to lie on. As he stretched out for a rest Mike realised he had no idea what the time was. He wasn't even sure what day it was any more, and he wasn't bothered about it either. He had no wristwatch to distract him now – it was tucked away safely on board; all he knew was that whilst it was still daylight the boats were to be kept moving, ever onwards. A sense of timelessness overcame him and as the sun warmed his limbs and the breeze played in his hair Mike took stock of his adventures so far.

Though it was barely four days since he had joined the boats Mike was surprised at how quickly he had become used to this strange and hard way of life. Getting up early was still a bit of a trial for him, but nothing could beat the taste of a cooked breakfast eaten in the fresh morning air, and that alone was worth getting up for – never mind the excitement of wondering what adventures lay ahead each day. He had overcome his distaste at using the Elsan lavatory, and in fact quite enjoyed his visits to the warm, cosy engine room. Sitting there in the half-light he would become mesmerised by the steady note of the pulsing engine, which was like a living creature, and each breath filled his nostrils with the heady smell of hot oil.

Each evening he and Kit would mop down the boats and polish the brass chimney rings and portholes, and together they would fill the big water cans – when there was a tap to provide a fresh supply. He had learned to be sparing with the fresh water from the cans, which was far more precious than the plentiful supply he was used to at home. 'For drinking and cooking only!' Mrs Coleman had once said, but they used it for most things – the alternative was to take water out of the canal, but no one fancied washing in that! At home Mike usually had a bath only once or twice a week, when his mother had the fire going specially to heat up the water. So he didn't miss the bathtub much, and was quite happy with his cat-lick wash in the dipper each morning.

Mike loved his food and so far he had enjoyed Mrs Coleman's cooking – and he had spent hardly any of his pocket money on sweets. He was working hard during the long days, and though his early breakfast and some thick sandwiches around mid-morning kept him going, he was always ready for the big meal later in the day. Mrs Coleman was right – working on the boats made him hungry! And as for drinks, there seemed to be an endless stream of cups of tea.

Then there was Kit. Mike felt that he was getting to know his new friend very well, and hoped their friendship would continue to grow. He liked Kit. They got on well together and he was a good teacher. Mike thought he was very lucky to be learning so much about the boats, the canals and his friend's special, secret way of life. And Kit seemed to like him, too. Mike smiled as he thought of the many laughs they'd already enjoyed together.

He shifted his position on the beam and, raising himself slightly, felt the muscles in his arms. But he had to admit that there was no noticeable difference there yet – despite his heroic efforts yesterday. However, he felt really fit and healthy, and after four days in the open air his skin had begun to turn a golden brown and his hair was going quite blond. 'This is really a fantastic life,' he thought to himself, gazing through half-closed eyes at distant birds wheeling effortlessly overhead. Beyond the birds, fluffy wisps of cloud were floating about, miles and miles above. Around him, though unseen, he could hear the gentle buzz of insects in the long grass. All that he could see and hear said to him, 'Freedom!' And in this blissful state he thought, 'It's a dream come true.'

'Oi! – Boats are waiting, Mike!'

It was Kit's voice, interrupting his daydreaming. Mike came down to earth with a bump – literally, because his friend's sudden shout had startled him and he dropped off the beam onto the rough brick paving beneath, his iron falling beside him, clanging on the hard surface. The boats were beginning to nose their way out of the full lock, so he leaped up at once and began to push the heavy beam on which he had been lying. The great gate swung slowly open, and the boats surged forward.

'Fancy the pictures tonight, Mikey?' shouted Mrs Coleman, poking her head out of the hatches as she passed him, leaning on his gate. 'We'll be near the town and all you youngsters can go off to see a film if you like.'

'Yes please!' replied Mike, immediately thinking of *A Hard Day's Night* again, and then dismissing the idea as being unlikely – unless Vince were going with them; but there was Susannah to consider as well.

'I haven't been to the pictures for ages,' he added, knowing that he would be glad to see whatever film was showing.

'That's settled then,' said Mrs Coleman, and she disappeared into the cabin. Vince, at the tiller, tossed Mike a couple of toffees wrapped in stripy paper as he passed, and then threw more to Kit at the gate opposite. 'That'll keep you going till tea-time!' he shouted to both of them. The two boys trotted together along the towpath, chewing at their sweets.

'Me Mum and Dad have started calling you Mikey,' observed Kit.

'Doesn't bother me,' Mike replied. 'Other people call me Mikey, or Mick, but I don't mind. At school my friends call me Wally,' he confessed. 'Wally Walker.' Kit sniggered at this. 'And I get called all sorts of things at home!' Mike added, grinning. 'But don't worry, I won't be calling you Kitty!'

'You'd better bloody well not!' exclaimed Kit, and he began to beat Mike playfully about the shoulders. Mike dashed off up the path to escape his friend's blows, and the two boys raced all the way to the next lock.

Later that day the landscape around the canal changed dramatically. Gone were the wide views across fields to distant woods and hillsides. Gone were the picture-postcard scenes of pretty villages with warm-coloured, red-brick houses, and church towers peeping out of the trees. The outskirts of a large city began to close in around the canal. At first it all looked friendly enough, and it reminded Mike a little of his own home town. From somewhere among the crowding houses he could hear the tinkling chimes of an ice-cream van. To its cheerful accompaniment, echoing far and wide, people were doing Saturday things. Here was a neat and well-kept park, with brightly painted swings and a slide. On the broad expanse of grass children were playing football and chasing dogs, the sound of their excited voices ringing in the air. Some children near the water's edge actually waved as the boats went past – the first time that Mike could recall anyone taking any notice of them, and he waved back vigorously. A group of cyclists zoomed by on the towpath.

They passed suburban back gardens, each very different, each saying a little about the people who lived there. Some had lush beds of flowers and plots of vegetables, another had hen coops and chickens strutting contentedly about. Some were well tended and neatly clipped, others were unkempt or cluttered with piles of junk, some had dogs which ran up and down and barked at the boats as they passed. Here and there Mike spotted a pigeon loft, or a greenhouse, and in one garden an outdoor model railway. There were people relaxing in the sunshine in their gardens; there was a man building a shed, and another man was taking his motorbike apart.

In turn these scenes changed too and the canal became hemmed in by old brick walls and taller, shabbier buildings that blocked out the sunlight. Many of them were disused or derelict and some looked as if they might tumble into the water at any moment. Weeds as big as trees grew from their walls and roofs, and broken windows revealed desolate interiors, long empty of people, long silent with disuse. Mike noticed a lot more rubbish in the cut, where the water looked black and lifeless – surely no fish or plants could live in such murk, beneath that oily surface. Fragments of wood drifted by, the remains of shattered packing cases; shapeless bundles of rags and old sacks lay just beneath the surface – waiting to wind themselves around propeller blades. Near the edge of the water rusty skeletons of bicycles, a refrigerator, oil drums and other discarded objects showed above the surface.

Gone was the towpath of trodden earth with grassy, flower-dotted borders. Now a black and grimy cinder trail accompanied the water, backed by rusting corrugated-iron fences, barbed wire, or warehouses and factories. Some of these used the canal as a drain, and pipes stuck out from walls. Some poured noxious-looking fluids into the cut, whilst others shot jets of steam across the water. Roughly painted on one wall Mike saw the slogan 'Ban the Bomb', and wondered who was meant to notice it written there.

The boats passed an old wharf and, standing on the gunwale of *Cepheus*, Mike peered beneath the overhanging awning at what had once been a busy warehouse. Rusting cranes, motionless near the water's edge, had long ago loaded and unloaded countless cargoes. Then the huge building had bustled with activity and echoed with the sound of workmen's voices; now it lay empty, silent. Broken light-fittings dangled on long wires, swinging to and fro in the breeze. With disgust Mike noticed the only other movement in the building – a dozen or more large brown rats scurrying amongst the piles of rubbish strewn across the concrete floor.

'Ugh!' he said aloud. 'Look at them! They're horrible.'

'Welcome to Brummagem, Mikey!' said Mr Coleman, who had passed these scenes dozens of times before. 'Or as you probably call it – Birmingham.'

Mike remained silent and stood gazing at the long succession of jumbled buildings stretching down the canal. Not all were decaying and abandoned like the one they had just passed. Many still showed signs of life, and some were quite new. There were factories, a wood yard, warehouses and offices. Electric lights could be seen dimly through grimy windows. There was an occasional whirr of unseen machinery, and here and there ventilator fans turned behind dusty grilles in the walls. But all these premises appeared to have turned their backs on the canal, ignoring the waterway that had once brought them into existence and helped them prosper. As they neared the city centre, however, they began to meet many more craft on the water. Boats were going back and forth, and boats were stopping at wharfs loading and unloading goods – mostly coal. There was still local traffic around the city, it seemed, and the canal was quite a lively thoroughfare as a few boatmen busily carried on their age-old trade.

In the distance, above the uneven roofline of the old buildings, Mike could see towering blocks of offices and flats glittering in the afternoon sunshine. Their windows reflected the sunlight, and their white walls stood out brightly against the blue summer sky. Away from the tired remnants of the old waterway a New World was being created in the city centre, a modern world which even from a distance looked exciting and attractive. But it was a world which appeared not to want the canal any more.

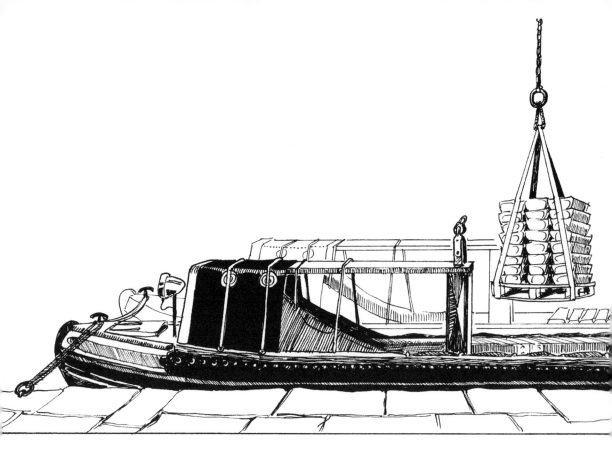

17. Family Reunion

As the boats approached the place where they would unload, Kit and Susannah were jumping up and down with excitement at the prospect of spending Saturday night in Birmingham. Suddenly Susannah gave a cry, and Mike thought she was going to fling herself off the boat.

'It's our Joyce!' she shouted, pointing into the distance and waving her hands wildly in the air. She called out, 'Joyce! Joyce! Cooee!' and looking ahead, Mike could just make out someone waving back to them from a boat tied up at a wharf. In fact there were several pairs of boats, and people were milling about near them – it was easily the busiest scene Mike had encountered since his adventure began.

The boats slowed and as Mr Coleman steered *Cepheus* towards the wharf where Joyce was still waving, the butty drifted alongside and soon both craft were being secured at the mooring. They'd hardly touched the side before Susannah had leapt off and was skipping along the concrete quay to fling herself into Joyce's arms. The two girls hugged and kissed, for it was several weeks since they had seen each other.

'Thought you might be appearing soon,' said Joyce. 'Mr and Mrs White was 'ere this morning, an' they said they'd passed you yesterday. And . . .' she went on, 'you've got a surprise for me, haven't you; a new member of the crew?'

'Oh yes!' said Susannah, who had so many things to tell her sister that she didn't know where to start. 'He's called Mike, and he's been with us for nearly a week. He's Kit's friend really, but we all like him. This is him!'

Mike was approaching the two girls, accompanied by Kit, whose arm was around Mike's shoulder as he talked excitedly about what happened at the wharf and what they would be doing later in Brummagem.

'Hello Mike,' said Joyce.

'This is our Joyce,' said Kit, proudly introducing his big sister and allowing himself to be hugged and kissed – though he pulled a face rather than kiss her back.

'An' she's been dyin' to meet you,' added Susannah.

'News gets around on the cut, Mike,' said the older girl, who looked with amusement at his wondering expression. 'We don't have no telephones, and we don't write – well, not much anyway – but the old "Cut Telegraph" works better than anything else. If you want somethin' to get around, tell a boatman – or woman!'

'Pleased to meet you,' said Mike, trying to remember his manners. He wasn't usually shy, but felt rather in awe of Joyce, whom he had expected to look more like a teenager. She was certainly a good-looking girl, with long dark hair falling down her back. But, dressed in a rather plain skirt with a bright pink cardigan and stout shoes she looked older than her eighteen years. He thought that if she had been in jeans and sneakers, with her hair in a ponytail she would have looked very like his sister Marilyn.

'Are you havin' a good time, do you like being on the boats?' she asked.

'Oh, it's smashing. I love it!' Mike replied. 'And I'm having a super time; it's the best holiday ever!'

'Mike's been workin' really hard,' said Kit. 'He's learned lots about boating already – and he hasn't fallen in yet, neither!' At this everyone laughed.

'What are we gonna do tonight, Joyce?' asked Susannah, and soon all four of them were deep in plans. Swimming baths were mentioned, and the pictures, and milkshakes at the cafe, and fish and chips for tea. But first of all there were important jobs to do at the wharf – less exciting for the Coleman children, perhaps, but all new experience for Mike.

'You'll prob'ly get unloaded very quick,' said Joyce. 'There haven't been many boats here today, and the men are just hanging around.'

Kit told Mike how they sometimes might wait for hours, or even days, to get unloaded if the wharf was busy, or if they arrived too late at a weekend. As they stood talking they could see Mr Coleman walking along the top planks of *Andromeda*.

'Come on!' said Kit. 'Me dad's getting' the cloths off. We'd better give him a hand.' He hurried away, with Mike in pursuit.

All along the boats the tarpaulin sheets covering the cargo were held in place by strings stretched tightly from one side of the boat to the other. Kit and Mike began to untie these, and one by one the large top sheets were folded and removed. Other sheets beneath, covering the sides and attached to the gunwales of the boat, had to be rolled down and tied securely. With the sheets off Mike could see the top planks sitting on a structure of posts and stays that held them in place like a great tent frame. All this had to be dismantled too.

It was heavy work, and took a while, but when all was done the cargo lay exposed and ready for the cranes to lift it out. For the first time Mike could see the piles of metal ingots, stacked along the length of the hold, which had been brought all the way from the docks in London.

'What about that bit at the front?' Mike asked, pointing to the fore-end of the boat where tarpaulin still covered a few feet of the hold, looking like a large dog kennel.

'Oh that stays there,' said Kit. 'It only comes down if we go under very low bridges when the boats are empty. It's got a funny name; it's called the cratch.' Mike mentally stored the name along with all the other canal words he had learned in the past few days. 'It's the *cratch*,' he could be heard muttering under his breath several times that afternoon in an effort to remember, until Kit told him to shut up.

'Got any washing, Mike?'

It was Mrs Coleman, who had appeared from the butty cabin with a great bundle of laundry. 'I'm off to the launderette,' she said, 'and I'll take your stuff too.'

Mike quickly searched in his locker for dirty clothes and passed them to Kit's mum, who tied them up with all the other things in a bed sheet.

'Makes life easier today, that launderette does,' she said to Mike. 'We used to have to light a fire and boil up a tub of water on the towpath, and do all the washing by hand, and it took ages. It's done in no time now in those machines, and whilst it's washing I can go round the shops too.' With her bundle securely tied she bid everyone goodbye and set off towards the nearby street.

'You'd all better make yourselves scarce now,' said Mr Coleman to the children. 'The men will be unloading us soon and I don't want you 'anging around an' getting tangled up in chains or hit by the crane.'

'We'll go and see Uncle Alf and Auntie Daisy,' said Susannah, and she and Kit and Mike were led away by Joyce towards their uncle's boats. Vince remained with his father. He usually gave a hand with the loading and unloading – and sometimes got paid a few shillings too. Since the children hardly ever got pocket money he was always glad of the chance to earn some. Soon, his dad had said, he could be taken on as a proper mate, and paid a proper wage. Or if he liked, he could have his own boats; but Vince was still not sure that he wanted to stay on the cut. This was something they didn't talk about much, because it made Mr Coleman sad to think that the traditional life of his family was not going to be carried on – at least, not by his eldest son.

Meanwhile the others had gathered around the cabins of the boats that belonged to the children's aunt and uncle. Mike was introduced and glasses of squash were passed round, together with Auntie Daisy's flapjack cakes.

'Have they let you steer the boats yet, lad?' Uncle Alf said to Mike. He was a tall man like his brother and had a similar face, though more lined and older looking, and a bushy moustache bristled beneath his nose. He seemed rather fierce and hardly ever smiled; but Mike thought that there was a twinkle in his eye, as if he liked to laugh but didn't really show it.

'Not yet,' said Mike, 'but I've been watching like a hawk, and I'm sure I could do it.' From the moment that he joined the boats Mike had been hoping desperately that he would be allowed to steer. But as yet he knew that he was a very raw recruit and would have to wait a while before being trusted with the valuable boats.

'Give it time,' said Aunt Daisy. 'They'll have to give you a go sooner or later – or you won't be able to say you've really been boating.'

Auntie Daisy was very different from her sister-in-law. As Kit's mum was slim and red-haired, so Auntie Daisy was a big roly-poly woman with lustrous chestnut hair, streaked with grey, which she tied up in a sort of turban. She smoked cigarettes one after another and laughed a lot. When she laughed her whole body shook, and Mike could feel the boat quivering too.

They all began to exchange news; tales of people they had seen, relatives and friends they had heard about, and whispered rumours and bits of tittle-tattle from up and down the cut, which made everyone gasp. Expressions of surprise or delight were exchanged at each new revelation. After a while several conversations were going on at once. Susannah was asking Joyce for tips about doing her hair, and Joyce was anxious to show her little sister some of her make-up which she had begun to buy. Uncle Alf wanted to know from Kit how they had got on during their recent trips, whether the engine was behaving itself and whether they had had any trouble from hooligans, and rubbish in the canal, and poorly maintained parts of the cut.

Mike was left to talk with Auntie Daisy and she was keen to know why he had wanted to join the boats.

'What ever made you want to come messin' about on the canal, Mike? Wouldn't you have liked a nice holiday by the seaside instead?'

'But I love the boats, Mrs Coleman,' he replied. 'I think they're really great, and I love being somewhere different every day, and seeing new things and doing different jobs. I miss my mum and dad a bit, but I've made really good friends with Kit and Susie and Vince. I'm having a really fab time.'

'You'd find it a bit different in the wintertime, my lad; when the days are short and the mornin's are dark and cold. When it snows, and when the cut freezes over – you ask your friend Kit what it was like, that wintertime last year,' and she gave him a knowing look, which suggested that she needn't say any more on the subject.

Mike began to feel a bit doubtful, but he replied as honestly as he could. 'I still don't think I'd mind that. I'm sure I'd find it just as exciting, whatever the weather.'

'Oh well, it takes all sorts, I suppose,' chuckled Auntie Daisy, cheerful once again. 'It's work and a way of life for us, and we don't know any different. I daresay if I 'ad to live in one place all the time and leave my home to go to work every day, in some stuffy factory, I'd soon be wanting to get back to the boats – rain or shine!'

At that moment Kit turned to Mike. 'Look, they've started unloading,' he said, and pointed down the wharf to where the crane was lifting a stack of ingots from the hold of *Andromeda*. A man who had joined Mr Coleman at the boats was shouting instructions to the crane driver in his cabin. Across the wharf a gang of men received the swinging stack, guiding it towards its resting place before slipping off the chains that had held it. A foreman with a clipboard kept an eye on the operation, inspecting each new load to see that it was complete. The yard was noisy with voices and the rattle of machinery.

'It'll take them a while to empty both boats,' said Kit. 'Why don't we go and have an explore?'

'What about going for a swim?' said Mike, who was now beginning to feel the effects of several days without a proper wash, and longed to be immersed in water.

'Oh yeah! Much better idea,' said Kit. 'Anyone else fancy coming to the baths?' he asked. But the girls were not keen and Joyce, jumping up suddenly, said, 'I almost forgot, Susie, I've got something for you.' She disappeared into the space behind the butty cabin and emerged seconds later with what Mike thought was a large bicycle tyre wrapped in colourful paper. But the wrapping did not deceive Susannah, whose face lit up with delight as she exclaimed, 'A hula hoop! Oh Joyce, how did you know I wanted one? Thanks ever so much.'

Soon the girls were totally absorbed as Joyce coached Susannah in the method of swinging her hips and twisting her body to keep the plastic ring spinning around her waist. Hula hoops were the latest craze and Susannah had seen many girls and boys with them, and had longed for one of her own.

Kit and Mike wandered back to the boats to get their swimming things and to tell Vince and his dad where they were going. The unloading had stopped for a moment whilst the men enjoyed a cigarette and a mug of tea.

'Meet you later, then,' said Vince, 'and we'll go to the pictures. I'll tell me mum that we'll have our tea in town – get some fish and chips, eh?' This arrangement met with the boys' complete approval.

The baths were only a short walk from the wharf and soon the two boys were splashing about in the clear blue water. Mike gave his friend some rudimentary swimming instruction and Kit managed to swim several yards in a very individual style, but without touching the bottom or swallowing too much water. He was very pleased with his progress and persevered, even though the baths were very crowded. He had to thread his way carefully through water fights, dive-bombers and someone performing underwater handstands, but he grew more and more confident as he went. Then he rested for a moment and watched Mike swimming. He envied the way his friend sped effortlessly through the water, his snaking body reminding Kit of the sleek pike and carp that he'd often seen flashing through the reeds around the boats.

Much soap and shampoo was consumed in the shower afterwards as the two friends had a thorough scrub, relishing the limitless flow of piping hot water. As they stood together in the steam Mike noticed how well developed Kit's muscles were, especially his torso and arms, which fairly rippled as he moved his body beneath the shower – the result of years of winding paddles and opening lock gates, Mike supposed. He hoped that working on the canal might improve his own rather skinny physique.

'Won't need to wash for a fortnight now!' shouted Mike afterwards, as he stood in front of a mirror carefully combing his hair. Dried and dressed he felt very clean indeed and ready for his evening out in town. Kit gathered up his things, playfully messed up Mike's hair again as he skipped past and said, 'Come on, Don Juan. I'll race you back to the boats,' and he dashed for the door.

It was about five o'clock when Mrs Coleman returned with her bundle of clean washing and a bulging shopping bag. The two boats lay emptied beside the wharf, their vast open holds had been swept and the stands and planks were replaced loosely inside them. Climbing into the hold of *Andromeda* the boatwoman busied herself rigging up a linen line. One end she hung from the short shaft (or boat hook) propped up like a linen-post by the cabin, and stretched the line along to the towing mast near the cratch. Then, whistling a cheerful tune, she began to hang out the washing, which was soon fluttering in the afternoon breeze, adding a touch of colour and gaiety to the drab surroundings.

Moments later Mike and Kit ran clattering back into the yard, their race from the baths ending in a dead heat. As they stood panting beside the butty, Mike was surprised at the changed appearance of the boats which, relieved of their heavy cargo, were riding high in the water. The deep sides of their blackened hulls were now revealed and it was much harder to climb up into the butty hatches from the towpath.

Vince was ready and waiting. Wearing a clean white tee-shirt and his leather jacket he sat in the sunshine listening to pop music on his portable radio. The younger boys added their wet swimming things to the washing on the line, then quickly changed into clean clothes. As they struggled into the smartest shirts and trousers they could find, Mike asked Kit, 'What happens now that the boats are empty?'

'We go off to the collieries and load up with coal to take back down south. It goes to one of the fac'tries on the way to London.'

'Oh yeah,' said Mike, 'I remember now. I've seen boats loaded with coal going through the locks by my house.'

'Anyway, forget about that now!' protested Kit, hopping up and down like a boxer and punching his friend playfully. 'We're 'aving a night off – and some fun, I hope!' And since he was now ready he scrambled out of the cabin. It was not long before Mike joined him, just as Joyce and Susannah appeared, coming along the quayside to meet them.

'Have a good time, all of you, and don't go gettin' into trouble,' said Mrs Coleman. She gave Vince some money for their bus fare and their tea; and Joyce said she would treat them all to the pictures.

'Off to the "Flea Pit" then, are you?' said Mr Coleman, popping his head out of the engine-hole doors. 'Don't be bringing any bugs back 'ome!' and he disappeared with a chuckle.

'Me dad thinks he's *so* funny,' said Kit to Mike, with a sigh.

'I expect you'll all 'ave a good natter in the pub while we're out,' said Joyce to her mother, with a wink. 'Auntie Daisy has got loads of things to tell you.'

'There's a few friends here tonight that me and your dad want to catch up with,' Mrs Coleman replied. 'People we 'aven't seen for ages. So I 'spect we shall make an evening of it.'

'See ya later, alligator!' they all cried, and Mrs Coleman shouted after them, 'In a while, crocodile!' as they hurried off down the narrow lane from the wharf and into the busy city street.

18. Downtown

The navy blue and primrose-coloured Corporation bus bobbed and swayed as it trundled toward the city centre. Everything seemed frighteningly fast after several days of the slow and steady progress of the boats on the canal, and Mike clung tightly to the back of the seat in front of him. Sitting upstairs he and his friends had a good view of the turmoil of Birmingham's Saturday rush hour, with motor cars, buses and bicycles crowding the road. Swarms of people scurried past the imposing office buildings, the big shops and department stores that lined the streets. The roar of the traffic was almost deafening through the windows, which were fully open to relieve the heat of the summer evening.

The conductress approached them, and after Vince had handed her a couple of shillings the uniformed woman reeled off five long green tickets from the machine she wore slung round her neck. Then she dipped a hand into her leather money-bag and passed a few pennies change to Vince. The bus had stopped meanwhile, and as she moved on down the gangway the conductress tugged at the bell cord twice and the vehicle slowly gathered speed again. The children chattered together and Joyce continued to share news with her brothers and sister. A whirring, buzzing sound, like very loud bees or a circular saw, caused Mike to look out to the road below, where he saw three lads having a race on motor scooters. Wearing smartly pressed trousers and dark glasses, each boy's hair streaming in the wind, they were bent over their handlebars, swerving in and out of the lines of traffic. Then they roared past the bus and sped away. Mike noticed that Vince had fallen silent and was watching the bikes too, a sort of far-away look in his eyes. Mike said nothing, but looked instead at the shops they were passing.

Compared to the little shops in his home town Mike thought these city stores very sophisticated indeed. He pressed his nose against the glass beside him and peered out. In the large plate-glass windows he could see the latest men's and women's fashions; jewellery, stylish hats and furs; up-to-date furnishings and electrical appliances; televisions, washing machines and record players. There seemed to be no end to the things you could buy for the home, or of clothing and luxuries. It all seemed far removed from the simple lives of the boat people. His attention was only diverted when Vince passed around some more of his toffees.

'What are we gonna see then?' asked Susannah at last.

'Let's see what's on first,' said Joyce.

'I want a film with some action in it,' said Vince. 'What about you, Kit-an'- Mike?'

'I don't wanna see nothin' sloppy an' sentimental,' said Kit with a scowl.

'Well, I think the Beatles are fab,' said Mike, 'and I really want to see *A Hard Day's Night*.'

'Won't let you in,' said Susannah, smugly. 'It's for adults.'

'I'll go in first then, and let you in through the side door,' Vince said to the other two boys with a conspiratorial wink.

'Vince!' cried Joyce, who looked shocked. 'It's all right for you and your mates to lark about, but don't go getting our lads into trouble.'

'I fancy seeing the Beatles too,' said Vince, 'so let's see if we are allowed in – legally.'

'What about you, Susannah?' Joyce asked. 'You haven't said what you'd like to see.'

'A musical!' Susannah shouted, without any hesitation.

'*A Hard Day's Night's* got songs in it – that's a musical,' said Kit.

'You know what she means,' said Joyce. 'A film with romance and singing and dancing an' all.'

The boys groaned and cast their eyes up at the ceiling, though Mike only did so because of the others. In fact he had enjoyed going to see Tommy Steele films and other musicals with his mum and sister. But he was not going to say so now, or Kit and Vince would certainly make fun of him.

'A musical it is then, for you and me – if we can find one,' Joyce said to Susannah.

They had reached the centre of town by this time and had begun to pass cinemas on the main streets, all advertising a variety of films.

'That one's got *A Hard Day's Night*!' shouted Mike suddenly, as he spotted the title illuminated above the entrance of the Odeon cinema. He leapt up in his seat and pointed out of the window as they passed. 'And it's a "U" certificate, so we'll be able to get in,' he added triumphantly, and a cheer went up from the other boys.

The bus drew into the main bus stop and everyone scrambled down the stairs and tumbled out into the balmy evening air. It was not quite six o'clock and there was an interesting mixture of people coming and going on the streets. Some were in their office and work clothes, still on their way home. Others in fashionable dress were the first of hundreds who would gradually fill the city again in search of entertainment.

Joyce led the way and the others followed in her wake, walking up and down a couple of streets looking for a film for Susannah and herself. Their search ended when they reached the ABC, which was showing *Wonderful Life*, the latest musical starring Cliff Richard.

'That'll be good,' said Joyce. 'I really loved *Summer Holiday*, and I bet there'll be some fab songs in it!' Susannah seemed pleased with the choice too.

'Looks like everyone is gonna be 'appy, then,' said Vince. 'You take Susie to see Cliff, and we'll all go to see the Beatles.' And so it was settled.

Since the next house was not till 6.50 for the girls' film and seven o'clock for *A Hard Day's Night* they all piled into a nearby Milk Bar for some refreshment. Mike had never been in such a place before, and he felt very grown-up and sophisticated sitting with Vince and Joyce amongst so many smart young people. The jazzy interior sparkled with brightly coloured neon lights reflected in white-tiled walls and mirrors. There was a hubbub of voices, and over all the conversations and laughter a jukebox belted out tunes from the current Top Twenty. At the bar a young woman was dispensing milkshakes from polished chrome machines.

'What's everyone want?' asked Joyce, who gave the orders to the waitress, and soon each of them was slurping delicious milkshake through a straw – banana, strawberry, chocolate or vanilla. When Vince had finished he nudged the two younger boys and nodded towards the counter. 'If I had a job away from the cut, I could chat up a girl like her and go on dates an' everything. It's no good though when you have to move on the next day and you don't know when you'll be back again.'

Kit and Mike nodded sympathetically, and the three of them sat silently gazing across the bar.

Joyce and Susie exchanged glances. Then Joyce broke the spell by putting sixpence into the jukebox and selecting three records. They listened to the Honeycombs singing 'Have I The Right', followed by Dusty Springfield and 'I Just Don't Know What To Do With myself'. Finally (for the boys' benefit) the strains of 'A Hard Day's Night' filled the long and spacious bar and everyone tapped their feet and waggled their heads or strummed imaginary guitars. They were all excited at the prospect of the films they were about to see, and because they thought there might be a queue at the cinema they didn't linger too long in the Milk Bar but were soon out on the street again.

By now there were more people about, bent on having a good time. Smart-suited young men escorted pretty girlfriends in beehive hairdos. Clusters of giggling girls walked arm in arm, intent on finding boys for the evening; and there were the boys in groups, swinging along the streets, hands in pockets, in search of young women. All were scrubbed and groomed and dressed in their best; swaggeringly confident or shyly self-conscious, but enjoying being the object of attention. Saturday-night Birmingham was coming to life.

'Meet us by the Milk Bar afterwards,' Joyce instructed as they parted on a corner, and the girls made their way down the next street. The boys were glad to be a bit early because there was already a long queue outside the Odeon and they hurried along to join the end before it grew longer still.

'Coo! That was lucky!' Mike suddenly cried, spotting a notice near the glass entrance doors. 'It says "Last Night Tonight" – and it's been showing for four weeks. Wow!'

'I'll treat you to this, Kit-an'-Mike,' said Vince, who had begun to speak to the boys as though they were one person not two. 'Joyce was going to pay, but we're split up now and she must have forgot.'

'Thanks, Vince,' said 'Kit-an'-Mike' together – as if they *were* one person!

When it came to their turn Vince could only afford two-shilling seats somewhere near the back, but the screen was very large and they snuggled happily into the deep, plush luxury of the upholstery and waited for the show to begin.

It was a huge cinema. Mike had never been in anywhere so big. It was dark and there was a stale smell of cigarettes and orange peel. Around them several people had lit up, and a wispy smokescreen hung above the ranks of seats that fell steeply away below them to the foot of the stage.

Soft lights played onto the elaborate curtains draped across the screen, slowly and subtly changing colour. One moment they were green, and when you looked again they were blue, then deep magenta, or gold. Then the dim house-lights dimmed still further, loud and brassy music struck up and the adverts started before the curtain had gone up, giving the images a strange rippled look. The curtain duly rose and the adverts were followed by a brief newsreel film – which most of the audience talked through. Then there was a cartoon and a short comedy film about the adventures of 'Ma and Pa Kettle' and their Hillbilly family. Everyone cheered and laughed at the slapstick fun.

After this the lights came up again, slinky music played and uniformed girls appeared as if by magic all around the auditorium. Each carried an illuminated tray of ices and drinks. Mike had brought some of his pocket money from the tobacco tin and he decided that it was now his turn to treat his friends. Clambering out of his seat he skipped down the sloping gangway, two steps at a time, to join the queue. 'Two choc-ices and a Mivvy, please,' he asked the girl when his turn came, and he added a large bag of popcorn for good measure – this was supposed to be a treat after all. His hands full, he gingerly threaded his path back through the milling audience and managed to reach his seat without dropping or squashing anything.

'Thanks, Mikey,' said Vince.

'Ta very much, Wally,' said Kit with a wink, and at that moment the screen burst into life again with trailers for forthcoming films.

'Can't wait for our flick,' Mike hissed to his friends through a mouthful of ice cream.

'Should be starting soon,' Vince whispered back, and all around them the theatre throbbed with tense excitement. When the opening titles of *A Hard Day's Night* presently flashed onto the screen, and the first chord of music sounded, the effect was astonishing. The whole cinema erupted with deafening screams and shouts and stamping of feet. Jumping and waving, young people almost flung themselves out of their seats, such was the thrill of seeing and hearing their idols on the screen, and Mike felt the floor tremble beneath him. It was a long time before the frenzy subsided and everyone settled, and even then the audience was never quite still. But Mike and his friends relaxed and sat back to enjoy the fun and antics of John, Paul, George and Ringo, and to tap their toes to the infectious beat of the music.

The film was everything Mike had hoped and more, and he whispered to Kit, 'This is fab!' Then he and the others became totally absorbed by the action on the screen. The canal and the boats, the locks and tunnels were all forgotten things, a million miles away.

'What a film!' Kit enthused, as the national anthem played and they joined the general stampede of excited youngsters clattering down the echoing staircase to the exit doors at the side of the cinema. Still buoyed up by the thrill of the film, they spilled out onto the pavement.

'I wouldn't mind seeing it again,' Mike replied.

'I wouldn't mind having a record player,' said Vince glumly, 'so that I could play Beatles records whenever I wanted – another good reason to get off the boats.'

'Don't be like that, Vince,' said his brother, 'you can still hear them on your radio.'

Dusk had fallen, and the air was cool. As they strolled through the illuminated streets they recalled their favourite bits of the film excitedly. They argued about which one of the Beatles they thought was the funniest (though all of them seemed to agree that it was Ringo) and sang snatches of the catchy songs they had heard.

They found Joyce and Susannah waiting outside the milk bar with broad grins on their faces.

'What was yours like,' asked Vince, 'any good?'

'Same as yours,' said Susannah.

'We went to the Beatles after all,' said Joyce, 'and it was brilliant, wasn't it?'

'What 'appened to Cliff then?' asked Kit.

'Well, when we got to the ticket booth we asked the girl what the film was like, and was it as good as *Summer Holiday*. She said she didn't think so. There was only one good song in it, she said, and that if she was us she wouldn't bother. So we just looked at each other and said "Beatles!" And then we went runnin' after you, but you'd already gone in.'

They continued to swap enthusiastic comments about the film, all talking excitedly and at once, no one listening to anyone else. So Susannah gave up and simply skipped along in front of them instead, singing 'I don't care too much for money, money can't buy me love . . .'

Another bus ride took them back towards the wharf and, as they went along, so the glamour of the bright city gradually dimmed and departed. Stepping off the bus and watching its red tail-lights disappear round a bend they found themselves in the dingy little street near the canal once more, a short walk from 'home'. A couple of gas lamps burned fitfully, but only seemed to make the surroundings drearier. It wasn't even really dark yet, anyway. The summer sky was still bluish above them.

'There's a great chippy along 'ere,' said Kit to Mike as they began walking. 'I'm starvin', an' I bet you are too.'

It had been a great night out, and this was the perfect way to finish it off – standing in the queue inside the warm chip-shop. The appetising smell of frying was overwhelming, so that Mike's hunger pangs grew almost unbearable. Vince had enough of his mum's money left to stretch to a bottle of Vimto each and Joyce dipped into her purse to pay for the fish and chips. The five of them walked home happily munching their supper from the newspaper wrappings.

Lights were still burning brightly aboard their uncle and aunt's boats as they picked their way across the clutter of the wharf, and they stopped there first, intending to say goodnight to Joyce.

'Did you have a good time?' Auntie Daisy asked as they stepped aboard the butty, and this was the cue for them all to start talking excitedly once more. Kit's mum and dad were in the cabin with Uncle Alf and Auntie Daisy. There wasn't room for all nine of them to squeeze into the tiny space, so the youngsters gathered around the hatches. Still feeling exhilarated by their evening 'Downtown' the children chattered about all they had seen and done. Their parents and aunt and uncle admitted that they had only just got in from the pub, and spoke of the many old friends they had met there, and what a merry time they had all had. Above them a broad moon, almost full, had risen into the sky and was shining brightly. Auntie Daisy made cocoa and Kit was sent to fetch extra cups from the cupboard on *Andromeda*. Another hour passed in cheerful conversation before someone noticed that Susannah, though she was propped upright between Joyce and Mike, had fallen fast asleep.

'Time for us all to leave you in peace, I think,' said Mrs Coleman, stretching her tired arms and rising to her feet. Susannah awoke with a start as the others climbed off the boat one by one and plodded wearily back to their own boats, which lay in shadow further along the moonlit wharf. Susannah leaned heavily on her mother as they walked, and could be heard faintly singing 'It's been a hard day's night, I should be sleeping like a log.'

19. Dirty Work

Mike was to find leaving 'Brummagem' a very different experience from his arrival there. 'Get yer oldest clothes out today, Mikey!' Mrs Coleman instructed him the next morning. 'This next stretch is gonna be a bit mucky, and I don't want to upset your mum by ruining your best outfit.'

As soon as they were dressed that Sunday morning Mike and Susannah walked to the paper shop down the road, a little way from the wharf. Mike wanted to buy a *Beano* comic, and Susannah had been sent for a newspaper. 'We'll meet you down by the locks,' she said to her dad, who was preparing to set off. Her aunt and uncle's boats had already departed, but the family expected to be together again in a few days' time, further along the cut.

The little corner shop was doing a brisk business and delivery boys were coming and going on their bikes, heavily laden with bags of Sunday papers. But away from the newsagents everywhere else was deserted. To catch up with the boats Mike and Susannah had to wander through several streets, Susannah skipping along leading the way. The whole city seemed to be slumbering. There were few people about and very few buses to be seen. It couldn't have been more different from the crowded and lively city of the night before. 'I 'spect everyone is still in bed, having a lie-in,' said Susannah. 'It's not very often that we can do that on the boats.' An occasional car passed noisily, but the only other sound was that of church bells pealing from an unseen tower nearby, and more bells could be heard faintly in the distance, like an echo. Mike and Susannah played a game with their reflections in the plate glass windows of a big chemist's, and then they peered at the displays in a toy shop, pointing out to each other all the attractive (and expensive) toys, models and games inside. 'There's some lovely things,' said Susannah, with a sigh. 'But I don't think I want anything else; not now I've got my hula hoop. You'll have to have a go with it, Mikey. It's a bit tricky, but it's great fun.'

'Hmmm, okay,' Mike answered without much enthusiasm. 'Perhaps I'll have a try later.'

From the main streets Susannah led Mike down a shabbier side street and then along a littered and smelly alleyway before diving through a narrow opening in the rough brick wall. Mike darted through after her to find some ancient and worn steps that led down onto the towpath beside the canal – completely hidden away from the city. On the other side of the opening they stopped short and their giggling voices ceased abruptly. They had almost fallen over what looked like a pile of old boxes and rags. But the pile shifted slightly as they stood there, frozen to the spot. They had stumbled upon a poor tramp or down-and-out who had spent the night there in that filthy hideaway, and now they had disturbed his sleep. A few empty bottles lay beside him and as they stepped carefully over him Mike inadvertently sent one of them crashing down the steps. The man woke with a start and began shouting at them in a slurred and aggressive voice, and they were frightened. Without waiting to apologise or ask if they could help, the two children just ran like mad down the steps and out onto the path beside the waterway. They ran hard for about a minute before daring to slow down, reducing their pace to a steady trot.

Stopping to catch their breath they laughed aloud at nothing in particular – a reaction to the fright they'd just had. 'You often see old men sheltering under bridge 'oles or in empty warehouses along the cut,' said Susannah. 'Drunks usually, but not always; and sometimes there's women as well. It's sad, really. I mean, there don't seem to be anyone to 'elp them. And not far away there's loads of people with lots of money and all the rich city, and shops and banks and everything.'

Mike made no reply, but reflected that he was really seeing life from many different angles on this trip. He'd never seen real poverty or need before, and now he'd actually touched it, in the form of the old man sleeping rough on the streets.

Rounding the brick abutment of a bridge a few moments later they spotted ahead of them the stern of *Andromeda* in the distance, and they quickened their step a little.

'It's very dirty, this stretch,' said Susannah. 'And on this canal we have to bow-haul the butty, 'cause the locks are smaller.'

While Mike was puzzling over this they caught up with *Andromeda* where she lay waiting at the top of the first lock, which Mike noticed was only half the width of those he'd been used to. He couldn't see *Cepheus* anywhere, but he could hear the engine and the sound of familiar voices nearby.

Soon Kit came running up. 'This is gonna be hard work today, Mike,' he said. 'All the locks on this canal are narrer ones. They only take one boat at a time. So the motor goes on ahead with me dad, and then *we* bow-haul the butty through – that means we have to pull it ourselves. You'll soon get the 'ang of it!'

And Mike did get the hang of it, though it was easily the dirtiest job he had ever done in his life. At each of the locks the chamber had to be filled again after *Cepheus* had gone through and emptied it. Then Mike joined Vince and Kit in pulling the butty into the lock on a long line, each of them passing the rope over their shoulders and stumbling along together on the rough towpath. This wasn't as hard as it might have been because the boats were empty. But this part of the canal was filthy dirty, all coal-dust and oil. The ropes picked up the dirt and the grime and soon the boys were covered in it. 'You wouldn't think I'd been to the baths yesterday,' laughed Mike after they had been working down the locks for an hour or two. 'I'm dirtier now than I was before I went!'

'Think yourself lucky it's not raining,' Vince answered. 'Then it's like rolling yourself around in pools of black paint! At least everythin' is fairly dry today.' They sang songs as they pulled their load along – rather like sailors from long ago, singing shanties as they hauled up the sails or wound the capstans to raise the anchor on the old sailing ships. Only these modern-day navigators sang songs from the film they had seen last night, and any other pop songs they could remember. For a while Mrs Coleman's washing still fluttered from the line on *Andromeda*, adding colour to the scene and looking rather like a string of signal flags on an old 'Man-o'-War'. But the clean clothes were soon gathered in so as not to spoil as the boat went down in the locks.

Mrs Coleman steered the butty and produced orange squash or cups of tea for everyone, to keep them in good spirits. Susannah sat on the cabin top of the motor and tried reading bits of news to her father. He was interested mostly in the accounts of yesterday's football matches and of a particularly daring bank robbery in Manchester. 'Read that bit again, love,' he would say to Susannah, when he couldn't quite believe his ears. 'They stole how much? Thirty thousand! Blimey!'

They passed a power station billowing smoke, its tall gantries and chimneys towering over the waterside; they passed several wharfs where boats were tied up ready to load or unload, though no one stirred on this bright Sunday morning. They passed factories and plots of derelict land and gradually the heart of the city was left behind, and their passage lay instead through dreary suburbs. They passed lots of Sunday fishermen, dotted along the towpath. Slumped over their rods and mesmerised by the bobbing floats in the water, they seemed almost to resent the passing of the boats and only one or two of them acknowledged Vince's cheery greeting from the tiller of *Cepheus*. At one lock where a road passed, there was a little shop nearby, and as they waited for the lock to be ready Mrs Coleman darted off the boat with her purse and returned a moment later carrying a package wrapped in newspaper. 'Something special for our tea,' was all she would say when Kit asked her what she had bought; and she gave a wink as she popped below to stow her mystery parcel.

Their peaceful progress that afternoon was marred only by some local children who had gathered on one of the bridges looking for sport. The bridge simply crossed the canal and made no connection with it. There was no way up from the towpath and the scruffy little gang must have known that no one could reach them from the water. As the boats passed beneath them on their vantage point they shouted, 'Yah! Gypsies!' and threw down stones. Fortunately their aim wasn't very good and most of the stones went into the water, but several hit their target. The Coleman family must have been accustomed to this kind of assault, for the children disappeared inside smartly. Mike, who was standing on the gunwale beside Mr Coleman, didn't move quickly enough. A particularly large stone bounced off the cabin top, narrowly missing him, and almost made him lose his balance. The trouble was that standing on the boats they were an easy target, and there was nothing they could do except wave fists and shout angrily at the grinning youngsters. The butty, following behind, was subjected to the same treatment, then the kids ran off and disappeared down a side street.

Vince peered out from the cabin doors. 'They'll prob'ly be back at the next bridge'ole,' said Mr Coleman. 'We'll get 'em, then,' said Vince, rubbing his hands together with glee, 'because the towpath goes up there.' 'Don't go making trouble,' his father replied. 'They'll just be worse next time they sees boats going past.' 'Not if we give 'em somethin' to remember us by!' said Vince with a grin.

Kit reappeared. He told Mike he'd once bought a catapult because he thought it would be a good way of getting his own back. But his mum had refused to let him use it. 'She said I'd be no better than them if I started hittin' back,' he said, gloomily – because he felt that she'd been right.

The gang of children could now be seen assembling themselves on the parapet of the next bridge, armed with replenished stores of ammunition. Not wanting to suffer the same treatment a second time Vince and Kit hatched a plan together and clambered forward along the length of *Cepheus* until they were both poised on the fore-end. 'You can join in if you want,' Kit called to Mike, who stood hesitating by the cabin. As the boat reached the bridge-hole, and just as the first stones were about to rain down on them, Vince and Kit leapt ashore and ran like mad up the sloping path and onto the bridge, taking the children by surprise.

'Gypsies are we?' shouted Vince, fixing the boys with his hardest stare.

'Throw stones at our boats, would you?' shouted Kit, and the two lads began to tussle with the nearest members of the gang who were now panicked and looking around for the best route of escape. Mike – who had jumped off the back of the boat – came panting up to the bridge and stared in amusement at the scrappy fight. Then Vince grabbed a boy – one of the biggest, but still small compared to him – and with Kit's help they up-ended the lad and lifted him over the parapet of the bridge. Suspended by his feet over the water he began first to shout in protest, and then to scream. Some marbles fell out of his pocket and plopped into the water below. A few of the boy's mates tugged at Vince's shirt sleeves and shouted, 'Put him down mister, we didn't mean no 'arm, it was only a bit of fun.' Other members of the gang scattered and ran away, pursued by Mike who dodged this way and that, growling and snarling at them like an Alsatian dog chasing burglars, and calling them all the worst things he could think of.

'Don't let us catch you doin' it again – or I might lose my grip next time,' Vince warned, pulling the boy back over the parapet and setting him on his feet, red-faced and shaking. He said not a word, but as soon as his feet touched the ground he bolted away down the lane as fast as he could, turning only to shout from a secure distance, 'I'll get my dad onto you! Yer big BULLY!' He then ducked as Kit sent a large rock flying in his direction, though deliberately aimed over the boy's head.

'I don't think they'll try that again in a hurry,' said Vince as Mike returned to join them and all three sped along the towpath to catch up with the boats.

Mike wasn't quite quick enough to jump onto the motor with Vince and Kit at the next bridge-hole, so he waited until the butty came past and joined Mrs Coleman in the hatches.

'Having fun!?' she said with a smile. 'I don't think Vince should have been quite so daring, he was a bit naughty really – but it was very amusing to watch!'

'Mum, why do they always shout "Gypsies" at us?' said Susannah, emerging from the safety of the cabin.

'Oh, I don't know, love,' her mother replied with a sigh. 'I s'pose it's because they know nothing about us, and they don't understand us, and they think we're different from them – like another race, or something. And that's the way they think about the Gypsies too; they must think we're all the same.

'People used to be afraid of Gypsies, you see, and all sorts of bad rumours were spread about them – only through ignorance. Gypsies are perfectly good people, of course, but they have their own ways and they keep themselves to themselves – which is a bit like us, I suppose. But Gypsies are free people; they do what they like and go where they will. And we're not like that, because we follow the same routes and do the same jobs, most of the time.'

The journey that Sunday ended amidst the rather bleak surroundings of a colliery and the rusting machinery of the loading wharf. The wharf lay down a quiet branch off the main line of the canal, and though not very picturesque it was at least peaceful. Nothing would happen until the men's shift began in the morning, so the evening meal was eaten on board in a leisurely way, after the boats had been mopped down and the brasses polished as usual. The wireless was switched on and everyone felt relaxed. After demolishing the lovely pie that Mrs Coleman had baked the children were eager to know what was for pudding. 'Well, there's fruit for us adults,' said Mrs Coleman, 'but – there's Mrs Baker's chocolate cake for you kids, and ICE CREAM to go with it!'

'Yippee!' they all chorused, for in the excitement of Saturday night and all that had happened that day, they had forgotten about Mrs Baker's gift. Now it seemed like a real treat – especially with chocolate ice cream too.

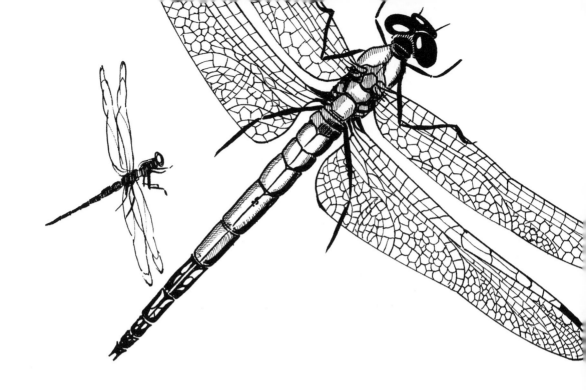

20. Another Cargo

Though the colliery wharf with its ancient machinery and shabby buildings was rather grim, its surroundings were strangely rural. Scrubland stretched away in all directions, dotted here and there with the artificial shapes of spoil tips and slagheaps. Early in the morning the scene was lent a strange beauty by the white mist that lay thickly on the water and the low-lying scrub. The rising sun cast a pink tinge in the mist and the sky, and glinted off the bearings of the conveyors and the wheels of the loading gantry, which were shiny with years of wear.

Mike wasn't aware of any of this at first, for he was fast asleep. At about five o'clock he was woken by the sirens of the colliery, signalling the start of a shift. Soon his half-awake head was jolted into consciousness by the chuffing of a shunting engine, the clanking of railway wagons, and the thundering of the cascading coal, which rocked the boat as it poured into the hold of *Cepheus*.

'You boys stay put for the time being,' Mr Coleman shouted to them through the doors of their cabin. 'An' keep everything closed till I tell you, or you'll be covered in coal-dust.'

Already Mike recognised the acrid but pleasant smell which he knew from the coal bunker at home. He also knew what coal-dust was like when it got into your skin or eyes, because he had experienced it the day before. Men's voices could be heard directing the operation on the wharf, and peeping through the porthole Mike then encountered the eerie but beautiful scene outside and the shadowy figures moving about in it. Vince was up, helping his dad, but Kit was still dead to the world. This place, this activity, must be so familiar to him, Mike thought, that he could sleep through it without difficulty.

After a while, when the commotion had stopped and there was relative peace outside, Mike heard Vince shouting and there came a banging on the side of the cabin. 'Come on, Kit-an'-Mike! You can start putting the cloths up and mopping the boat down.'

'Okay!' came the muffled and sleepy reply from beneath Kit's bedclothes, and first one arm and then the other appeared, stretching into wakefulness.

When the boys were ready and had climbed out onto the stern of *Cepheus* they could see that the boat had been moved along from the loading gantry and *Andromeda* was now lined up in its place, awaiting its share of the load they were to carry. The hold of the motor was filled to the brim with shiny black coal, which rose up in four mounds in a line. The boat lay low in the water, even lower than it had been when carrying the ingots. Because there was a danger of water spilling into the hold when the boats were in the locks, Kit explained, it was necessary now to put the side cloths back along the boat, tying them over the top-planks. But the coal didn't need to be covered completely, so the remaining tarpaulins were left off.

Kit directed his friend's unsure hands as the cloths were unrolled and pulled into place. Mrs Coleman came along to help them, for the tarpaulins were heavy and the strings that held them up had to be pulled and tied very tight. It took a long time before the cloths were all neatly secured, and the lads were exhausted. But before they took a rest for breakfast they carefully mopped all the coal-dust from the paintwork and decks until the boat looked neat and bright once more.

After breakfast the butty was treated in the same manner, and around about nine o'clock both boats were ready to set off down the arm and back onto the main line. Soon the day had turned into a real scorcher and Sister Molly's calamine lotion was never more welcome. Everyone got burned, and was eventually streaked with the soothing pink stuff across the neck, or the forehead or nose, or down the forearms, until they looked like Red Indians in war paint.

There were no locks for an hour or so and the boys were able to sit undisturbed on the fore-end of the motor. Some of the time they talked, but for long periods they simply lay in the sun and watched the world drift past. Occasionally an iridescent dragonfly would appear alongside the boat, hovering for a moment near where the boys lay before dipping away across the water, its busy wings barely more than a haze about its stick-like body.

'Kit, what was it like on the boats the winter before last?' said Mike, after they'd been silent for some minutes.

The question puzzled Kit, who gazed around him at the blue sky and the heat haze rising from the lush summer landscape. 'Whatever brought that into your head?' he replied.

'Oh, nothing. It was just something your Auntie Daisy said to me the other day. She didn't think I'd be so keen on boating in the wintertime.'

'Well, what was it like where *you* live, winter before last?' said Kit, throwing the question back to his friend.

'Terrible!' was Mike's reply. 'But I really enjoyed it.'

'An' it were terrible for us too!' said Kit. 'And I wouldn't say that *I* enjoyed it – not much, anyway.'

'Everything in school froze up, and we couldn't go back after Christmas,' said Mike. 'We had about three days' extra holiday.'

'Not really "terrible" then,' said Kit. 'No wonder you enjoyed it!'

'The lavatories were frozen, and they had to put paraffin stoves in them to thaw them out. And when our milk came in at break-time it was frozen as well. The cream was sticking out of the necks of the bottles with the silver caps perched on top. We had to put it on the radiator pipes to thaw it out. And I got lots of chilblains on my toes,' he added, wincing at the painful memory.

'We got well and truly stuck,' said Kit. 'Stuck for weeks. First, it just got cold and snowy – but we've 'ad that lots of times before. But then the ice started. We was able to break it up when it was only thin, by steerin' slowly through it. But it builds up in the locks, and when you breaks it up the lumps get stuck behind the gates. You have to move 'em around wiv poles, and push 'em out of the way.'

'Did you do that?' Mike asked.

'We took turns, but it was me dad and Vince, mostly. Me and me mum did the steering. Yer 'ands soon get so cold that you think they're gonna drop off. An' the ropes freeze an' go all stiff, an' they're hard to use.'

'But you kept going?'

'As long as we could. But then the ice went thick an' solid an' not even the ice-boats could make much difference – it just froze up again after they'd been through.' Kit added, 'The ice-boats are special ones, pulled by lots of 'orses. They smash the ice and clear the road for the other boats.'

'What happened then?' asked Mike.

'We didn't 'ave much choice,' his friend replied. 'We 'ad to stop where the ice had got us trapped. We were headin' for a little town by the next locks, but it got colder and colder and then we was stuck, about half a mile short.'

'How did you manage, then?'

'Well, we was warm enough, because luckily we had a load o' coal on, an' we didn't see why we should freeze as well, when we had tons of fuel. We 'ad to walk to the village most days though, to get food and water. And sometimes we spent an evening in the pub. But after a while the shops and pubs began to run out of things too – food an' that – because the roads was blocked as well, you see.'

'Yeah, they were blocked around us too. I went out with my dad, on a walk, and outside the town the snow was as high as the hedges, and only the tops of the bushes showed you where the road went. It was just huge snowdrifts as far as you could see. The trains stopped as well, for a few days.'

'Well, we was stuck for weeks, like I said.' Kit looked gloomy. 'An' that was the start of the trouble, my dad says. All the factories was waitin' for their coal, and the other things that go on the boats. The roads got cleared well before the canals unfroze, so lots of things was carried by lorry instead.

'It's getting harder work on the cut now; less and less stuff's going on the water. More and more of it's going on the roads. It's not just 'cause of the bad winter, though, as some people says. There's other reasons, like the canal not being prop'ly looked after. The government's not interested in canals anymore; they don't wanna spend money on dredging, or repairs and modernisin'. Tha's why me dad thinks we might have to chuck it in soon, but I don't want us to.'

'Did you get paid while you were frozen up?' asked Mike.

'Dad had to go and find work on the land. He got a job shovelling salt into the lorries that was going round clearing the roads. An' our Vince got a job too. There was a motorbike workshop in the town and their lad was ill, so Vince 'ad about six weeks' work there. That was where he started going mad about bikes, an' wantin' to be a mechanic and everything. So that's another thing me dad blames on the freeze-up – for turning our Vince against the boats.'

Both boys were silent for a moment. The deeply laden boats were still moving, the steady chugging of the engine could be heard away behind them, and around them the birds sang and the wind was having fun making waves in the cornfields. All looked peaceful and unchanging. There were no roads nearby with rushing and roaring traffic to remind them of the threat which hung over the boaters' way of life. Yet they were both thinking, 'how could all this possibly come to an end?' The sadness of the thought seemed for a moment to overwhelm them.

'*You'll* carry on, though, won't you?' Mike broke the uneasy silence. 'Don't you want to have your own boats?'

'Course I do,' said Kit. 'But you can't run a pair of boats on your own, you need at least two. I'd have to find someone else to do it with me. I could just run a motor by meself, I s'pose. But it depends on whether you can get the loads to carry.'

Mike could see the predicament, and began to realise for the first time that this wonderful trip he was enjoying was perhaps more precious than he had first thought. In a few years' time the boats, the families, and the cargoes going up and down might all be gone. He felt particularly sorry for Kit, because it was obviously the way of life he loved. A thought went through his mind. What if *he* were to come and work on the boats; work with Kit on a pair? He'd have to wait until he was old enough to leave school though, and his mum and dad wouldn't understand, he felt sure. There seemed to be so many obstacles, once you thought about it, but it was an exciting idea. Before he could think any more about it, however, his daydream was abruptly ended when he heard his name being shouted.

21. A Surprise for Mike

'Mike!!' It was Mr Coleman's voice.

'Me Dad wants you,' said Kit, whose gloomy mood disappeared instantly. There was a twinkle in his eye as he added, 'Better go an' see!'

Mike clambered up onto the top-planks, shuffled quickly along to the cabin roof and dropped down onto the counter where Mr Coleman was steering.

'Here I am,' said Mike, who was a bit worried in case he had done something wrong and was about to be told off. 'What's up?'

'Your first steering lesson is up, Mikey, me old son!' said Mr Coleman cheerily.

Mike's face beamed. He could hardly believe it. Of course he had been hoping and hoping, and looking forward to the day when he might get a chance to steer the boats, but he had almost given up thinking about it. Now he was very excited – and more than a little nervous.

'This is a quiet stretch,' went on Kit's father. 'It's not too windy, and there's no locks for a bit. So, look and listen, for a start.'

Mr Coleman pointed to the two controls mounted beneath the sliding cover of the cabin entrance. On the left was a small brass wheel, about four inches across. On the right was a much larger one which always reminded Mike of the handle on his mother's sewing machine – and on which he had banged his head a few times, climbing in and out of the cabin.

'This 'ere is the speed wheel,' said his instructor, indicating the smaller of the two.

'I know,' said Mike eagerly, 'I've watched how you use it loads of times.'

'Good lad,' Mr Coleman went on. 'I know you've been keen, and you've been watchin' carefully. But I'm just making sure you've got the right idea! Wind it one way, anticlockwise, and we slow down; back the other way and we speed up. Have a go!'

Mike turned the wheel gingerly, the engine revved and he felt the craft surge forward as it gathered speed. Then gently turning it in the opposite direction the boat slowed until it had resumed its former pace.

'Not bad, not bad! Now – this whopper on the right,' and he pointed to the sewing-machine handle, 'this is the gear wheel for forward and reverse, an' at the moment you don't need to touch that at all – or we shall be in a right mess.'

'Okay,' said Mike obediently, looking up at Mr Coleman's face with anticipation.

'Now, swap places with me and take the tiller.' As he spoke, Mr Coleman stood aside and, putting his arm around Mike's shoulder, guided him into position in the space between the cabin doors.

'Grab the tiller, lad. Don't be afraid of it.'

Mike grasped the shiny wooden handle at the end of the polished brass shaft. It vibrated a little in his hand as turbulent water from the propeller blades pummelled the rudder below.

'Whoah!' Mike exclaimed. 'It feels really funny; it's like it's alive!'

'Just 'old on tight, and try moving it a tiny bit to the left and right.'

Mike stood gazing fixedly ahead along the length of *Cepheus*. He had stood at the stern many times before; but now that he was actually in control of the craft himself it looked a very long boat indeed. Before him, over the roof of the cabin, the line of top-planks stretched ahead to where Kit's face, tiny in the distance, grinned at him from above the cratch. His dad had told him earlier that he was going to surprise Mike by letting him steer today, and Kit had agreed to stay out of the way so that he would not put his friend off. 'I don't want you larkin' about and making the boy nervous,' his dad had said.

With his arm bent behind him, and leaning on the cabin slide in the way he had seen so many other steerers standing, Mike gripped the tiller more firmly and pushed it slowly to the left. Immediately he saw the bows of *Cepheus* respond by turning towards the right of the waterway.

'Not too far,' said Mr Coleman quietly, 'we don't want to go aground. Bring her back to the centre of the cut.'

Mike drew the tiller back, and pushed it a little to the right. As he did so the bows returned to the centre of the canal and then continued over towards the left.

'Straighten up, straighten up,' coaxed Mr Coleman, still giving his instructions calmly, so as not to unnerve Mike in his first attempt.

Mike pushed and pulled the tiller a little at a time until the long craft was motoring in a straight line again, down the middle of the cut.

'Very good, very good. We'll make a boatman of you yet!' said Mr Coleman. 'There's a few more things to learn, but that's a good start.' This was a huge understatement, and Mike knew it, but he felt encouraged by his words.

'It won't be long before you're taking us into locks, and winding the boats – that's turning them round – as well. But all in good time. You carry on steerin' for a bit, and just get the feel of it. You mustn't be afraid of the boat. You've gotta feel more like you're a part of it.' Then he added, 'Your first obstacle will be comin' up soon, but don't panic, I'll be here with you.'

Mike concentrated hard and with some help from Mr Coleman managed to keep the boat in the centre of the canal. Occasionally he turned round to look at *Andromeda* as if he were afraid that it might not still be following behind, but Mrs Coleman merely smiled and waved to him reassuringly from the tiller of the butty. Mike's glimpses behind were very brief – he didn't want to take his eye off the way ahead. The boats approached a bend and Mr Coleman guided Mike's hand on the tiller, making sure that the craft turned in exactly the right place.

'Take it right across,' instructed Kit's dad, 'and wind the engine on a bit.'

Mike leant heavily on the brass shaft, pushing it hard across, and with the engine revving, the boat glided gently round. A new stretch of canal opened up before him and he saw a bridge-hole in the distance. Mike straightened the boat and reduced the speed.

'That's your first obstacle,' Mr Coleman said, with a smile. 'Now, just aim the fore-end at the middle and keep a sharp look out ahead in case there's boats comin' on from t'other side.'

As the bridge drew nearer Mike felt like he wanted to close his eyes, or hold his breath. Instead he concentrated as hard as he could. He gave a couple of turns on the speed wheel and slowed the boats down a little, and was rewarded by seeing the bridge pass by without a bump or scrape. For a moment the engine noise echoed loudly off the arching brickwork; Mike's hand strayed back to the speed wheel and soon the boats were moving faster once again. From the fore-end Kit could be heard applauding his friend's efforts. 'You're a natural!' he shouted to Mike.

Mr Coleman was nodding his head slowly in approval too. 'It was a good idea to slow down a shade, Mike. In some bridge'oles there's a chance you might ground on the mud or pick up rubbish if you goes too fast. It's a matter of knowin' which ones!'

'I was just copying what I've seen you and Vince doing,' said Mike.

'Well, carry on like that and you won't go far wrong,' Mr Coleman replied.

Mike was about to step aside, thinking that his trial at the tiller had come to an end. However, Mr Coleman made no move to relieve him of his charge, but shifted himself onto the gunwale at the side of the cabin where he leaned comfortably on the roof beside the chimney. From this position he was able to keep an eye both on the road ahead and on Mike at the tiller.

As the boats made their way along under Mike's control, Mr Coleman chatted to him in a confidential, friendly way. He told him about keeping to the deepest part of the channel; about how to take bends so that the butty followed safely behind; and then step by step he talked Mike through the process of taking the boats into a lock. 'An' one day, when you've 'ad a bit more practice, we'll let you try that as well,' he said to the bemused Mike, whose head was swimming with so many new things to remember.

As Kit's dad chattered on in his gentle way, Mike started to relax. He felt some of the tension going out of his shoulders, and he began really to enjoy his steering. Under the experienced boatman's watchful eye and careful guidance he negotiated several more bridges and bends; and even passed an oncoming pair of boats. He was especially pleased when this happened because both the steerer of the other motor (a young man with a cigarette drooping from his lower lip) and the young woman at the elum of the butty greeted him with a nod and a 'How d'ye do?' and Mike acknowledged their greeting in exactly the same way. The young man held up four fingers to Mike and shouted, 'You've got four ready!' As the other boats passed on down the cut he asked Mr Coleman what this meant.

'They've left four locks ready for us, is what it means, Mikey. They've come down four locks without passin' another boat till they seen us. So, it means that them locks will be ready and waiting when we gets there.'

'Should I have let him know that we've left some locks ready for them?' Mike asked, anxious that he should do everything properly.

'Don't worry, lad,' Mr Coleman laughed. 'You *could* have, if we'd passed any, but we haven't done no locks today!'

'Oh, no. I'd forgotten,' said Mike, embarrassed at not remembering. When at last the locks, 'ready and waiting', came into view, Mr Coleman took charge of the tiller from Mike. 'Another day, Mikey,' said the boatman, 'another day.'

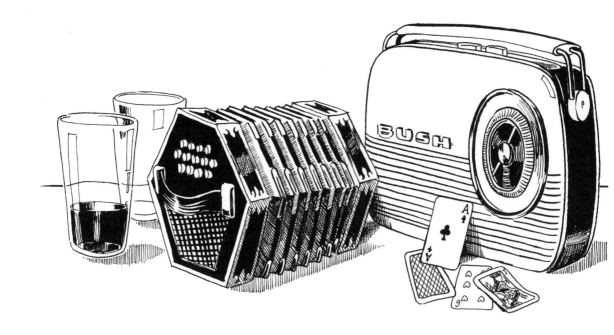

22. A Boaters' Gathering

That evening the boats tied up at a canal junction. Kit had said that it was a popular place for the boat families, a place where you could often bump into old friends, and Mike had imagined crowds of people and lots of activity. But it seemed rather quiet when they arrived and Kit remarked, 'Not many here today.' They passed few moored boats and there was plenty of room for them to tie their own pair.

A small office stood at the junction from which, so Vince told Mike, orders were issued to the boaters for the cargoes they were to carry and which colliery they were to load at, for there were several nearby. Therefore some of the boats were empty and awaiting orders whilst others, like the Colemans', were already laden with coal and tied up ready for an early start in the morning. Uncle Alf and Auntie Daisy had arrived earlier with empty boats. They would receive their orders from the office the next day. Joyce ran up to meet the children as soon as *Cepheus* and *Andromeda* were firmly moored. She looked anxious and a bit flustered.

'What's up with you?' Susannah said, sensing that her sister wasn't quite her usual self. Auntie Daisy passed by at that moment, water can in hand, and overhearing the question she shouted, 'Love sick! That's what she is!'

'Don't take any notice,' laughed Joyce, nervously twisting her hands in her apron.

'What's she mean?' said Kit.

'She's got a boyfriend!' shouted Vince suddenly, as it became clear to him why his sister was behaving oddly. 'That's why she's gone all gooey!'

'Shuddup, Vince! It's not like that,' Joyce said, and felt herself blushing.

'Bet it is,' said her brother, who was now completely convinced. 'What's his name?'

'None of your business,' Joyce said with some spirit. Then she said to Susannah, 'I was going to tell you the other day, Sue, but there never seemed to be a right moment.'

'You mean our Vince's right?' gasped Susannah, instantly pleased and excited. 'Oh, why didn't you say? Tell me all about him!'

Auntie Daisy was now passing back again, and without any prompting at all said, in a single breath, 'His name's Roddy Lee, an' he's twenty-three, an' he's been in the army, an' he's tall, dark an' handsome, and his boats are gonna be here tonight.' Then, drawing breath, she added, 'an' that's why she's moping about like a sick kitten and can't settle to anything.'

'Oh, Auntie!' sighed Joyce. 'You've spoilt it all now!'

Auntie Daisy (who was very matter-of-fact and quite hopeless at keeping secrets or confidences) looked wounded. 'Well, sorry love. But couldn't you see they was all agog, eager to know?'

'I s'pose I *have* been a bit slow,' Joyce admitted, laughing nervously. 'But, now you know everything.' Her words did not satisfy the others, but unleashed a bombardment of questions, all fired at once.

'Is he comin' tonight, then?' queried Susannah. 'Can we meet 'im?'

'What was he doin' in the army?' demanded Vince.

'What are his boats called?' asked Kit.

'How long have you known him?' Mike asked, not wanting to be left out.

'He was on National Service,' Joyce began, stepping back as if recoiling from the barrage. 'He had to do his bit in the army, but it was only for two years. An' he works with his dad and mum at the moment, on their boats, which are called *Spion Kop* and *Liverpool*, and I met him here about a month ago when there was a dance on. And you can meet him tonight – if he gets here,' she finished, 'but don't go makin' a fuss and annoying him.'

Without another word Susannah scampered back to the boats excitedly. Unable to keep the news to herself, she wanted to tell her mother and father straight away. Vince continued talking to Joyce and she teased him, saying it was about time he found himself a girlfriend.

'How do you know I haven't got one?' Vince bluffed, but his sister was not so easily fooled and just looked at him in a knowing way. It was Vince's turn to blush. 'You wait till I get my motorbike, they'll come flockin' then,' he said indignantly. But his sister just laughed. 'I'll find you a nice girl – someone off the boats, that's what you need. See ya later!' Before Vince could reply she ran off in pursuit of Susannah. Joyce was anxious that her parents should be given the news plain and simple, and was afraid that her little sister might be making up extra frills herself.

Meanwhile Kit took Mike to meet some of the other boating families. Each time Mike was introduced he was astonished at how much was already known about him.

'So this is your new steerer is it, Kit?' said one old man, with a wink; and then to Mike, 'How did yer like bein' in charge of the boats then, lad?' A young woman remarked to him, 'You're from orf the bank, ain't yer? Bet you won't wanna go back to your 'ouse when you've finished your trip!'

'You're right,' Mike replied, for that was exactly how he felt at that moment. He seemed to have been accepted by the boaters, and it felt good to him to be part of their roaming, nomadic world. But as he and Kit wandered around a note of sadness clouded his happiness. The boaters, whose conversations he overheard, were talking of families leaving the cut, or of boats being laid up and no cargoes to be had. Once again Mike couldn't help feeling that he was experiencing a way of life that was not to last much longer.

But joy returned and glum thoughts were put aside that evening. In the tiny, crowded pub it was just like old times. The boaters gathered to drink and talk and laugh. Later, as the evening mellowed, an old man was persuaded to take up his little concertina and lead everyone in singing some of the old songs of the cut. Those who could sing – and even those who could not – sang along lustily, and some of the older men and women danced the intricate and agile steps of old-time dances they had learned from their parents.

Encouraged by the appreciative crowd and by several drinks, a young boat captain produced his ukulele and entertained everyone with favourite music-hall songs. The low-ceilinged bar rang with happy uplifted voices, cares were forgotten, and tomorrow didn't matter.

Roddy's boats had appeared as predicted and Joyce proudly introduced him to the few people who had not met him before (because everyone knows everyone on the cut, or if they don't know them they know *about* them). He was a great success with the Coleman family and instead of spending the evening inside the pub with all the adults, Roddy sat outside with Joyce and the youngsters in the warm summer dusk. Roddy had made a special effort for his girlfriend and dressed in a smart stay-pressed suit, with a clean shirt and polished shoes – perhaps this was a habit from his military training. Joyce brought out a portable wireless from her boats and tuned in to some dance music. She and Roddy did the twist on the roof of the butty cabin to Chubby Checker's *Let's Twist Again*, and the others tried to imitate them. 'It's like watching the audience on *Top of the Pops*,' Mike said, but he had to explain what the TV programme was about. Tune followed tune, and they twisted and jived and cha-cha-cha-ed frantically until they were exhausted.

Afterwards Roddy entertained them with card tricks and stories of his time abroad with the army. Playing cards disappeared and were discovered up Roddy's sleeve or in Kit's shirt pocket. Roddy did impersonations of his old Sergeant Major bawling out orders, and of Jock and Geordie, two of his army pals. He was funny

23. Holiday Boats

Very early next morning, before anyone on *Cepheus* had stirred, there was a soft knocking on the cabin side. Because Mike was already awake (he was used to early starts by now) and because he was nearest to the doors, he pushed back the sliding cover and peeped out. After the stale air of the stuffy cabin the freshness of the morning breeze greeted him like a slap in the face, and even at this early hour Mike could feel the warmth of the sun. It was going to be another scorching day. Joyce was standing there beside the boats, her light cotton clothing fluttering in the wind. In her hand she held a writing pad and a ballpoint pen.

'Hello, Mikey,' she said in a whisper. 'Do us a favour, will you?'

Mike just smiled drowsily to indicate both 'Good morning' and 'Yes, okay.'

'Will you write me a letter, for Roddy, please?' she asked. 'I can write a little bit, y'know, but I 'spect you've got nice handwriting, and you can spell all the words better than me.'

This request took Mike by surprise. He didn't know that this was a quite usual request from a boater, and that those who had difficulty writing would often ask others to write for them – even personal things like letters to a sweetheart. But he took the pen from Joyce and set the writing pad flat on the cabin slide, then settled himself comfortably in the doorway and waited, pen poised.

Joyce, without any embarrassment, dictated her love-letter, saying that she liked Roddy very much, that he was the best-looking lad she had ever met, that she loved the way he laughed and that she couldn't wait till they were together again. She asked lots of questions about things that he liked – music and films – and what star sign he was.

'Do you want to ask him what football team he supports?' suggested Mike helpfully, when Joyce paused for more ideas. He watched her ponder this for a moment and then she said, 'No. Not really.' Instead she said something about herself, telling Roddy which pop stars she liked, and that she loved to dance, and that she was saving money to get some new clothes soon, and that she was a Gemini. Before long Mike had filled several sides with his bold but neat handwriting. Then Joyce signed her own name carefully at the bottom and put lots of kiss-crosses before folding it and sealing it in an envelope.

'What address do I put on it?' asked Mike, who found himself wondering stupidly whether boats had letterboxes. Joyce gave him the address of a canal office in the north of England and explained that Roddy's boats would be passing through there in a few days' time, when he would pick up his letter. Then she gave Mike a little kiss on his forehead, saying, 'Bye, Mikey. I hope I'll see you again, but I dunno when. Have a good 'oliday, though!' and she ran off to post her letter before joining her aunt and uncle, whose boats were now ready to set off. Mike watched her retreating figure and returned her little wave before she disappeared round a corner. Then he stepped back into the cabin where Vince and Kit were starting to get up. Soon the engine roared into life, the boat lurched as it took the weight of *Andromeda* in tow, and they were on their way once more.

'What's that, going on up ahead?' said Mike to Kit, who was at the tiller of *Cepheus* later that morning. Having watched his friend's steering lesson the day before, Kit had been anxious to show Mike how good he was at the job himself. And it was true that, having been used to steering since he was quite young, he was very competent. He didn't often get the chance to steer the motor, though, because his dad and brother did most of it. He'd seized his chance today when his father had wanted a rest (after his night in the pub) and Vince was steering the butty.

'Looks like a campin' boat,' said Kit, peering into the distance. It was difficult to see clearly because the sun was so bright on the water. He shielded his eyes with his hands and looked again.

'It's some Scouts on a hired boat, I think' he explained. 'Lots of people come on the cut now just fer 'olidays, 'specially this time o' year. Sometimes they use one of our boats, one like this, and they camp under the tarpaulins, like bein' in a tent. It makes a nice change, though, to see different people usin' the cut – so long as they don't 'old us up. Most of 'em knows that we 'ave to keep going, and they stays out of our way. They usually tie up early anyhow – they don't do the long days what we do.'

Over the past week Mike had noticed here and there along the canal a variety of boats besides the familiar narrow boats – many of them more like the pleasure cruisers you see on the river. He and Kit had laughed at the 'Captain' of one such boat, who wore a nautical cap and blazer as if he were in command of a yacht in the Mediterranean; but mostly the crews of the boats were cheerful, friendly people, obviously enjoying their boating as much as Mike himself.

As they drew closer to the lock that lay ahead Kit and Mike could see dozens of boys scurrying around the gates and jumping on and off their boat, which was waiting above it.

'We'll 'ave to slow down an' wait in the channel, 'cause it looks like they're gonna be ages getting that boat through,' said Kit. As the engine slowed down so Mr Coleman's inquisitive head appeared from the cabin where he'd been taking his nap. 'What's up, Kit? Trouble?' He climbed out and looked to see what lay ahead, then immediately took the tiller from his son's hands and steered the boats nearer to the towpath. 'You an' Mike jump off and go an' give them a hand, or we'll be 'ere all day,' he said. So Kit and Mike, armed with their irons, leapt off the boat as it neared the bank and ran to the lock to see what was going on.

At the lock-side confusion reigned. There must have been twenty or more boys about their own age, but they were not Scouts as Kit had at first supposed. If they had been Scouts they might have been more orderly and better supervised. Some of the boys wore odd items of uniform, probably from a boys' club somewhere, but most of them were in old clothes. There were two men with them who must have been leaders and were clad in baggy shorts, sandals, and shirts covered with badges. But although they were apparently in charge, they were not coping with the process of getting the boat through the lock. They ran up and down shouting instructions, but no one paid any attention.

'You've got too many paddles up!' said Kit to one of the men, after a quick look at the situation.

'Get lost, nipper!' the man replied, not noticing where Kit and his friend had appeared from. 'We know what we're doing, thanks very much,' he snapped, and waddled off to shout more ineffective orders to his crew.

Instead of attempting to explain more to the man, Kit simply grabbed Mike's arm and together they ran to the bottom gates of the lock, which teemed with boys. They were all shouting at once and fighting one another over who was to do what. Kit pushed firmly into the huddle, elbowing one or two out of his way, and lifting the safety catch on the ratchet he quickly dropped the paddle. At the same time Mike skipped across the gate and did likewise on the other side. The lock needed filling in order to get the boat in, and water was correctly pouring in at the top end. But with paddles open at the bottom end too it was emptying as fast as it filled.

''Ere, clear off!' cried one of the surprised boys. 'Wadderyerthinkyerdoin?'

'You're just wastin' water,' shouted Kit angrily. 'An' you'll never get your boat in if you 'as all the paddles up. *And* you're holding us up as well.'

'Now, now! What's going on here?' It was the leader again, hands on hips and breathing down Kit's neck. His colleague ran up to join him. 'S'pose you think you know all about canalling then, do you lad? And where did you get that windlass from?'

'I hope you're not one of these troublemakers,' the first man chimed in, 'going around emptying locks and damaging gates.'

At this Kit lost his temper.

'I WORK on the cut,' he shouted through gritted teeth, 'and I LIVE on the cut! I've been through these locks more times than you've 'ad 'ot dinners, AND I KNOW WHAT I'M DOING!'

There was silence. Then, in a calmer voice, Kit continued. Waving his windlass vaguely towards the top of the lock, he said, 'There's our boats behind if yer don't believe me. Only you haven't bothered to look to see if anyone was followin' yer. You're holdin' us up. We've got a load to deliver an' we don't get paid till it gets delivered. Now, let us 'elp you or we'll never get through. Haven't you ever done a lock before?'

The two leaders began to look sheepish and admitted that they had only started out that morning and this was their first lock. To save face one of them said, 'But we *do* know what we're doing – it's just that the lads are over-excited and aren't listening to instructions.'

Kit was not impressed. But by this time the lock was full and he and Mike stood back to see if the leaders could supervise the rest of the operation as they had claimed. With some difficulty the boat was manoeuvred into the lock, the gates and paddles were operated correctly, and the boat began to descend.

Suddenly Kit leapt to the lock-side shouting, 'Pull it forward! You're gonna get stuck on the cill!'

Panic broke out and the leaders rushed to get boys pulling on lines, but the boat was already caught and they couldn't move it. Kit barked instructions: 'Drop the paddles at the bottom; draw the top ones again – QUICK!'

Peering into the lock Mike could see that the boat was tilting at an alarming angle. The stern was caught on the ledge that protrudes below the top gates in every lock, and which good boaters carefully avoid. The bows were disappearing under water as the stern rose up behind. One of the older boys was standing at the tiller of the boat, but he was engrossed in a *Spider-Man* comic, unaware that anything was wrong. He sprang into life when he heard the shouts from the lock-side above him, but there was nothing he could do, the boat being stuck fast.

Obeying Kit's instructions the crew halted the flow at the bottom and began to fill at the top. After a few agonising moments the boat floated free and was level once more.

'You could've sunk it then,' said Kit, sternly. 'Keep it forward in the lock when it's emptying,' he warned, and the operation was begun again. The lock emptied successfully this time, the bottom gates were opened and the boat emerged and drew into the side ready to pick up its crew. Both leaders looked white and shaken and the company of boys was very subdued.

'Thanks very much, lads,' said one of the men, meekly. 'You certainly saved our bacon there, I think.'

'Want to see on board?' said the other man, in what seemed an attempt to make amends for their earlier rudeness. So Kit and Mike took a quick peep under the tarpaulins of the boat to see lots of bunk beds and little tables and benches, cooking stoves and sleeping bags. It all looked very cosy and well equipped, and seemed none the worse for its mishap.

'I hope you have a good time,' said Kit, who was always good-natured and had apparently accepted the men's intended apologies. 'But let us pass you once we're through the lock, will you, please? We're faster than you, an' we can't afford to lose time.'

'All right, lad, we'll hold on here and wait till you've got by.'

Mike had filled the lock again by this time and *Cepheus* motored in. The Youth Club boys and their leaders watched with careful interest as Kit and his friend pushed on the gates and wound and dropped the paddles in a smooth operation. Lots of questions were asked and answered; there was some laughter, and the atmosphere grew more friendly.

Before long *Andromeda* had been hauled in too (with the help of some of the other boys on the towing line), and was dropping in the lock. A small group of boys stared at the cabins of the boats. 'Cor! Is that where you live?' said one of them to Mike.

'Yeah,' he replied, nonchalantly and not entirely untruthfully. He felt a glow of pride as he realised they thought he belonged to the boats, and somehow he couldn't bring himself to spoil the effect by saying, 'No, I'm just here on holiday.'

Moments later they were on their way again, and the boys on their camping boat were soon left far behind.

'You sorted 'em out then, did yer Kit?' Mr Coleman asked his son. Kit looked at Mike, and the two of them raised their eyes skyward and laughed.

'I'm glad they're behind us,' said Kit, 'but I think they'll be all right now. I think they've learned how NOT to do it, anyway.' Mike continued chuckling to himself.

'Whassup wiv you?' asked Kit.

'"I've been through these locks more times than you've had hot dinners!"' squeaked Mike, mimicking his friend's angry voice. 'I've never heard that one before, but it's really funny!' and he chuckled again.

'Stop taking the mick, Mick!' replied Kit, and he began pummelling his friend with his fists, which made Mike giggle even more. Kit gave up his assault and laughed too.

The sky was cloudless that afternoon. Vince had made sandwiches whilst the boats were waiting, and everyone munched them hungrily in the fresh air, soaking up the warmth of the day as the boats ploughed forward.

24. Roses and Castles

'An early finish today, boys!' said Mr Coleman to Kit and Mike. 'We'll tie up 'ere.' The two lads were surprised, because it was only about four in the afternoon – well before the usual time for tying up. The boats had reached a junction near a large village and had joined a busier canal. Here there was a boatyard and a couple of wharfs. The boatyard lay up a short arm and a few boats were moored round about, the wisps of smoke curling from their chimneys a sign that boaters were aboard. There were other boats, however, that showed no signs of life and looked as if they'd not been used for a long time. Some were in a rather sorry state, half-filled with water, their paintwork peeling. Despite the activity around the boatyard, there was also an air of decay.

'We're well ahead, and this is a good place to get the engine seen to while we've got the time,' Mr Coleman went on. Although he'd replaced a part in the engine himself he was still not satisfied with the way it was running. 'So you lot can go an' explore – only don't be getting into any mischief!' he added firmly.

'Recognise this place?' said Kit to his friend. 'We're back on the main line again now. We've come a full circle from Brummagem, and now we're headin' back the way we come. Wide locks again now – so no more bow-hauling the butty!'

'I thought it looked familiar,' said Mike, 'but we didn't stop here before, did we?'

'Nope. We went straight through and up that way,' Kit replied, pointing to the junction and the branch of the canal that turned off westwards.

The two lads leapt off excitedly as Vince steered into the side, and both craft were quickly secured to iron rings set in the concrete bank. They were just about to rush off when Vince shouted, ''Old on a minute, Kit-an'-Mike! Mum wants yer!'

Mrs Coleman, who had been steering the butty, called them over and asked them to take Susannah and run up to the shops. The two boys exchanged looks of disappointment, but said nothing. Anyway, it would be fun to explore the village as well. They set off, crossed the water over a hump-backed bridge and followed the lane uphill to the village. There they found a few shops along the rambling main street, including a chip shop, and a couple of pubs too. In a past time the village and its canalside yards must have been very busy, serving countless passing boats and their families. It all looked a bit sleepy now. Tea-time was getting near and the smell of frying wafting from the chippy made them feel hungry. But there would be no fish and chips tonight – Mrs Coleman had a liver casserole in the range.

Soon the children were staggering back to the boats with bags of groceries. They found that Mrs Coleman had wandered off to borrow a sewing machine from one of the other boats. She had been given some pretty fabric and was going to make a skirt for Susannah. Mr Coleman and Vince were by *Cepheus*, leaning in at the engine room doors, deep in conversation with the mechanic whose muffled voice could be heard within. No one paid any attention to them, so they wandered off towards the untidy muddle that was the boatyard.

'Let's go and see Mr Fleet doin' some of his painting,' said Kit, his eyes lighting up with excitement at his idea. 'He's brilliant! You should see him doin' all the roses an' castles an' things. His workshop's over the other side. Come on!' And he led the other two across the cluttered and dusty yard, where rough balks of timber lay ready to be cut and shaped into new planks for boats, and where iron fittings of all shapes and sizes lay scattered in a disorderly jumble, along with rusting sheets of steel. The three of them played 'Follow My Leader' as they skipped along narrow lengths of wood and leapt over barrels and piles of boxes, before reaching a long row of low sheds which stood overlooking the canal arm. Pushing open a tired-looking old door, which was barely still on its hinges, Kit led them into a large airy workshop. There was a strong smell of paint and thinners, and an elderly man sat at a bench near the window, paintbrush in hand.

'Hullo, lads and lass!' said Mr Fleet. 'What can I do for you?'

'Hullo, Mr Fleet! We've brought our friend Mike to see your painting.'

'Well it's a pleasure to see you all, I'm sure,' the old man replied. 'You'll not mind if I go on working for the moment will you, only I'm quite busy this ar'ernoon?'

As Mike gazed at Mr Fleet he thought that he looked more like an old farm hand than an artist. But his idea of an artist was someone who painted portraits and landscapes with windmills, or pictures of Napoleon on his horse – the sort of paintings he had seen in galleries on school trips. Artists wore smocks and berets, and carried a palette with their colours on – at least that's what Mike had been led to believe. And they usually had a thin moustache and were temperamental. But Mr Fleet wore big boots, a battered felt hat and had large, clumsy-looking red hands. He screwed up his old and watery eyes as he concentrated on his work.

On his bench sat a water can, just like those on *Cepheus* and *Andromeda*. The paint was fresh and bright, and on a dark-green background a riot of colourful roses flourished, with a few daisies dotted here and there. A red band about the middle set off the other colours and the base was circled by a multi-coloured lozenge pattern, all adding variation to the lively design. In his hand Mr Fleet held a dipper – one of the long-handled metal bowls that all the canal boats carried, and which served many purposes. As they watched, Mr Fleet deftly added petals to the background blobs of colour that he had already painted so that with each swift curl of the brush beautiful flowers came to life in his hands.

'How long have you been doing this?' said Mike at last. He was completely captivated by the old man and fascinated by the ease with which he created such lovely images. Mr Fleet paused for a moment and scratched his temple with the end of his brush to aid his thought.

'I started these yesterday ar'ernoon,' he said, ' – but I've had one or two other things to do today as well.'

'No, I meant . . .' Mike started.

'Oh! You mean how long 'ave I been paintin' in me life!' said Mr Fleet, suddenly realising what Mike had really asked. 'Since as long as I can remember, my boy,' he went on. 'I first remembers watching me old granddad doing this, and learnin' some of the pictures from me dad too. They was both painters, afore me.'

Mr Fleet was obviously quite happy to talk, though his brush never rested for a moment. He went on to tell how many generations of his family had been involved not only with painting but in boat building and repairs too. He himself had been trained in many skills to do with boats, he said, and over the years he had turned his hand to any job that needed doing. Later, his own sons had taken over the heavy work and other men had been employed too – the yard had been a busy place in those days. But now when a boat came in for its 'docking' – the term which covered a multitude of jobs from repairs to repainting – he, old Mr Fleet, concentrated mainly on the painting side of things.

'There's a boat out on the slipway you can go and have a look at if you want to see more of my work. Painted the whole lot, I did – and I was glad of the chance too. We don't get so many boats these days, and I likes to keep my hand in; keep the old skills polished, so to speak,' and he chuckled quietly to himself.

Mike could see that Mr Fleet was a world apart from other 'artists'. No sitting around in fields or up mountains, waiting for inspiration; no studio or gallery; no throwing pots of paint at the canvas and pretending it was 'Art'. Every design that Mr Fleet painted had been painted before him by his father and grandfather. He had learned the patterns and the techniques as he had learned about life itself, and now he painted the same roses, the same castles, and the same traditional patterns that had adorned the boats for generations. He painted quickly, but Mike knew that behind the easy-looking strokes there was great experience and skill and that if he had picked up a brush himself the results would have been very messy and disappointing.

'You could do this,' said Mr Fleet, as if he had heard Mike's thoughts. 'Nothin' to it, really. Just a steady hand, some patience, and a few years' practice,' and he looked away from his work momentarily to smile broadly at Mike.

'Look at these!' It was Kit's voice, calling from another corner of the workshop. He had been exploring among the shelves and the stacks of paint tins, and had found a pair of cabin doors glistening with fresh paint, which were propped up near a stove to dry.

'Be careful near those,' warned Mr Fleet. 'They've been varnished this ar'ernoon, and they'll likely still be tacky.'

The other children gathered around where Kit stood, and admired the doors. In a small panel at the top of each was a miniature landscape, dominated by a castle with clustered towers. A long red pennant flew from the top of the largest tower. The castle overlooked a winding river crossed by a road on a hump-backed bridge. A pale blue sky backed the scene, dotted with feathery white clouds. It was the sort of scene you often saw in storybooks, which didn't look quite real but which you longed to step into. Looking at these panels now, Mike found himself wondering who lived in the castle; where the road led to; and whether it was always so sunny and peaceful by that still water.

'It's just like the ones on our Joyce's boats,' said Susannah.

'Almost, but not quite.' said Kit.

'We all has our own style, us boat painters,' said Mr Fleet. 'We all paints the same things, but very indervidule, if you gets my meaning. If I was to see the pictures on your sister's boats, I'd soon tell you who done them.'

Mike thought of the story of the Willow Pattern plate, which he had done at school; a design that was always basically the same, yet depicted with endless variety by each artist who painted it.

'This is lovely,' Susannah exclaimed. She had left the others and was looking at a tiny little stool that stood on Mr Fleet's bench, right in the window. It was very simply constructed but its beauty lay in the profusion of roses and daisies with which it was covered.

'Ah, now that's very special,' said Mr Fleet. 'That's to be a present, and I was asked partic'lar by someone to make that and paint it.'

'Who's it for?' asked Kit, who was never afraid to ask whenever he was curious.

'Old Mrs Hawkes,' said Mr Fleet. 'Old Ivy and her husband have had to leave the cut – too old now, you see. Well, they didn't want to go, no one ever does, after a lifetime on the boats. But still, they've got themselves a nice little house by the canal now, not far outside of Brummagem; and so's they feel at home their daughter wanted something they could have as a memento – off the canal, like. So we thought a little stool would be just the thing – for her to prop her feet on when she's sitting in front of her nice new gas fire. It's going to be a surprise. I hope she likes it.'

'I'd be very happy if someone gave it to me,' said Susannah. 'I'd treasure it all my life. What a lovely present!'

Mike thought of many things he'd seen in shops and had wished for as presents. But they were manufactured things, made by the hundreds – or thousands. Now he felt he could appreciate the value of something like this simple little stool. The craftsmanship in it, the thought in making it and giving it, and the special knowledge that no one else would have another quite like it. You couldn't have a better present than one that had been made especially for you.

'Ah, well. If I be still here when it's time for you to be wed, my lass, then I'll paint something special just for you. What do you say about that?'

'It'd be lovely,' said Susannah, and she smiled at Mr Fleet, and even dared to give him a little hug.

'Careful now!' he cried. 'All my roses are goin' to be wobbly if you do that too often.' But he laughed and said 'Cheerio!' as the three children thanked him and waved goodbye and trotted out of the door.

Susannah felt a bit sad. She couldn't help thinking that Mr Fleet was very old, and that by the time she was ready to be married he might not be around to paint a present for her. She shared her thoughts with her brother and Mike.

'Nope, I don't think he'll be paintin' for much longer,' Kit said. 'The boats are all gradually finishing, there won't be nothin' left for 'im to paint in a few years' time. An' I don't think anyone else has learned how to paint from him. When he's gone, that'll be the end of it.'

'Let's go and see his boat,' suggested Susannah, trying to cheer everyone up, and they made their way round to the slipway. From this concrete area in front of the largest shed, boats were launched sidelong into the basin. Standing on the concrete, on blocks at the water's edge, was a fine boat, its tarry hull the blackest of blacks and its paintwork shiny and colourful. It was all ready to return to the water and get back to work. All was prepared for its steerer and his family to set up their home again in the bright cabin. Soon there would be smoke from the cabin chimney again, and the brass rings would be brightly polished, the plaited rope-work scrubbed white. The boat had an air of hope about it which put the gloomy thoughts out of the children's heads, and they stood for a long while in silent admiration of the painter's skill.

25. Heading South

The next two days passed under the blazing sunshine of late August. Slowly but steadily the boats chugged southwards, daily approaching closer to their goal of London and the docks. Back through the two tunnels they passed again, where scorching day turned to damp and chilly night, and Mike was once again thrilled and a bit scared by the noisy, spooky and fume-filled darkness. And as they worked up and down the locks and around the pounds Mike recognised things he had noticed on the outward trip – here was the place where they'd got stuck on the rainy day; there was the pub where they'd tied up one night. By this time the routine of working the boats had become second nature to Mike; it felt to him as if he had been doing it for years. Each evening he knew he had earned his rest. When the noise of the engine was stilled so that skylarks could be heard across the fields, singing their hearts out as they rose up on the warm air, peace and contentment filled his body and soul.

The moment also came for the biggest challenge that Mike had yet been given. He had not expected to be allowed to do more than steer the boats between the locks, but on the second afternoon Mr Coleman put him in charge of the motor once again. After an uneventful hour at the tiller Mike could see the gates of a flight of locks rising up in the distance. 'I'll take over now, Mike,' said Mr Coleman, 'but you stay here and watch what I do very closely; an' remember all the things I told you.'

'Okay,' said Mike, and his brow furrowed as he tried hard to recall all the details in the right order. Soon the motor was passing between the massive black gates of the lock and Vince, who had cycled ahead, peered down at them from above. Kit stepped off the boat as they reached the lock and ran up to help his brother. Mike concentrated hard and took note of all that happened from the moment they entered the gloomy chamber until the boats had risen up to the higher level and were on their way out of the opened gates at the other end. He stayed put on the stern of the motor as they entered the following lock and the one after that. Each time he carefully followed the pattern of the operation as it was repeated.

Then, as they set off toward the next lock, Mike heard, 'Over to you now, lad!' and Mr Coleman stepped aside, putting Mike firmly back in charge of the craft. His mind suddenly went blank, his knees went weak, and everything seemed to swim before his eyes. ' I can't do it! I can't do it!' he said to himself. But then through his anxious thoughts he heard Mr Coleman's steady voice giving instructions, step by step.

'Slow her right down now, Mike, that's it.'

'Keep over to the right.'

'A bit of reverse now – that's right, turn the wheel all the way round. Give her a rev. Fine, fine.'

In a haze of exhaust smoke *Cepheus* nosed up to the end of the lock chamber and the butty came running in alongside, its towing-line slacking.

'Now lift the rope off the dollies; throw it over to the front of the butty; that's right, that's great.'

Above him on the lock-side someone slowed and stopped the butty with a rope thrown around a stout post. Then the gates swung to behind him and the dark slimy walls towered up above him on both sides.

'A few revs on the engine, Mike, keep the boat forward.'

As the lock filled Mike felt the surge of water lift the boats, sending them backwards in the lock. The butty strained on its line. He revved the engine again, edging

the motor forward till it nosed against the timbers of the gate in front. Diesel fumes and coal smoke swirled around him in the deep chamber. Gradually his head rose above the parapet of the lock and he was back up in the open air again, the lock nearly full.

'Now gently forward, give the gates a nudge.'

As Kit and Vince swung the gates wide Mike eased the motor out with a confident turn on the throttle. Then, on Mr Coleman's instruction, he picked up the rope from the front of the butty as he passed and looped it round the dollies, the little bollards on the back of the counter. As he went ahead the line at first ran free, then tautened, and Mike finally secured it with a final twist round the dolly as the butty followed him out of the chamber. He'd done it! He'd taken the boats through a lock!

'Can I hand it back to you now?' Mike said, urgently. 'I feel all shaky.'

'Of course, son,' said Mr Coleman. 'You done well there, but it's time for a break. Have another go tomorrow, eh? We'll be going "downhill" then.'

Mike didn't really suffer from nerves, but now that his ordeal was over he felt a bit overcome by it all and wanted to sit down.

'Can I make some cocoa?' he asked.

'What a good idea!' said Mr Coleman.

Towards the end of that day Mike felt a sense of foreboding as he realised that they could not be far from his home town. He asked Mr Coleman whether this was so, and was told that they would pass through it the next day, around ten o'clock in the morning. So that evening, after they had tied up, Mike walked away alone to find a phone box in the village and rang his neighbour. With Mrs Aldridge's number propped up in front of him he turned the dial with a heavy heart, for he was afraid that his parents would want him to finish his journey tomorrow, at the locks where he had begun it. But he wasn't ready to finish, he told himself; he wanted to go on and on. He wanted at least to go as far as the place where they were to unload their cargo and even, perhaps, down to the docks where the boats would be loaded again. It would be awful if his trip had to end suddenly the next day. There was a click, the ringing tone stopped and a woman's voice said 'Hello' and announced the number.

'Hello Mrs Aldridge, it's me, Michael. Can I speak to my mum, please?'

When he heard his mother's voice on the other end of the line a few moments later he began to gabble all his news at once, telling her what a fantastic time he was having, and asking finally that he be allowed to stay on the boats for a while longer. His mother wanted to know that he was well and that he wasn't being a nuisance to Mrs Coleman and her family in their work.

'No, Mum. Honest!' he cried. 'I've worked really hard, and they've let me steer, and everything – I even went into a lock today.' There was a cry of horror from the receiver.

'No! Not *fallen* in! I mean I *steered* the boats in.' Then he pleaded again, 'Can I stay on a bit longer then, Mum, can I?'

His mother agreed that he could stay aboard for two more days, but he would have to get the train back from London when they passed near a railway station. 'It's only a few days now before you start back to school, Mike, and you need to get yourself ready,' she said. And, just before Mike's money ran out in the phone box, Mrs Walker arranged to meet her son the next day at the locks, just to confirm everything with Kit's mother.

Mike replaced the receiver wishing that his mother had not mentioned school. But it was true nonetheless – his holidays were coming to an end. Still, there were two more days, he told himself. Two more days of adventure, two more days of excitement and discovery, because he would be passing new stretches of the canal that he had not seen before. Cheered by this thought and with a spring in his step he almost skipped back to the boats to tell everyone his news. But neither Mike nor any of his friends could have known what adventure lay in store for them all.

Mike hoped that some of his schoolfriends might be hanging around on the canal near his home, so that he could greet them from the boats. But he was sure it would be too early for them. It was about half past ten when they began to work *Cepheus* and *Andromeda* down the locks the next day, and Mike looked eagerly for his mother. When he spotted her, standing at the place where he usually lingered to watch the boats, he was surprised to see his sister Marilyn with her, and his Auntie Peggy too – so he had an audience after all. As Mike opened the gate and the boats crept from the empty lock, Mr Coleman shouted to him from the stern of *Cepheus*, 'Come on Mikey, over to you now. Show 'em what you can do!' Mike didn't hesitate but ran down the steps from the lock, two at a time, leapt aboard the motor and gratefully took the tiller from the thoughtful boatman.

'Try an' look natural and confident, like,' said Mr Coleman with a smile, and Mike adopted a very casual and nonchalant stance as he drew near to the lock below and the little crowd of onlookers.

'Mike's showing off!' said Marilyn to her mother and aunt. 'Bet he's just trying to impress us.' Which was exactly what Mike was doing. The fact was that – in Marilyn's case at least – he had succeeded too. She stared in awe at the two enormous boats and at Mike's tiny figure crouched over the tiller far behind. And secretly she was not only impressed but quite envious of him, for he was obviously having the time of his life.

As the boats entered the lock, greetings were exchanged with Mike's family and Mrs Walker rushed forward. She dipped a hand into her bag and produced a small black camera.

'Time for a snap, please,' she called cheerily. 'All hands on deck!'

'Looks like we're gonna have our picture taken, Mikey,' said Mr Coleman. 'So you'd better stay by that tiller for the moment,' and so saying he hopped across to the butty boat and stood in the hatches with his wife at the elum. Susannah climbed up onto the cabin roof in front of them and Kit, running up to the boats from the lock behind, took up his position next to Mike on the counter, with an arm around his friend's shoulder. Only with some difficulty could Vince be persuaded to join in. He'd been poised ready to draw the paddles at the bottom of the lock, but he wandered reluctantly along and stood by the boats on the lock-side, leaning on the cabin of *Cepheus*.

'Smile please!' said Mrs Walker. 'Watch the birdie!' And the shutter clicked, capturing in a fraction of a second a moment that was never to be repeated; a picture full of sunlight and colour and happy friends; a photograph that was to be one of Mike's most precious possessions for many years to come.

The clicking of the shutter was the signal for activity to begin again as everyone prepared to get the boats down the lock. But Mrs Coleman stepped ashore for a moment and Mike went with her to greet his mother.

'You look healthy and happy,' she said to her son; and, 'I hope he has been behaving himself,' to Mrs Coleman.

'He's been a great help this past week or so,' the other woman answered. 'We shall miss him when he goes.'

'So you don't mind him being with you for a couple more days, then?'

'Dear me, no!' said Kit's mum. 'We shall get a bit more work out of him yet!'

'There's some money here, for his train fare home,' said Mrs Walker, passing an envelope to the other woman, 'and this is for you all,' she added, handing over a large biscuit tin. 'I was baking yesterday, so I made you a fruit cake – as a little "thank you" for looking after him.'

'Very much appreciated, I'm sure. Thank *you*,' said Mrs Coleman who then excused herself and said goodbye to Mike's assembled relatives.

Mike greeted his aunt and sister and after quickly asking if Marilyn had had a good holiday, he said, 'Have to go now, got to keep the boats moving!' He was about to hurry away when his mother said, 'Why don't you show Kit around the town now you're here? I don't expect he's ever been beyond the towpath before – except to call for you.'

'Oh, Mum! I don't think we've got time,' and he looked anxiously at Mrs Coleman.

'You can go if you like,' she said. 'We can spare the two of you for half an hour, I expect.'

'I can show him around another time,' pleaded Mike, 'when they're passing through again. I'm still on my holidays now, Mum!'

'Oh, all right then,' his mother relented. 'You'd better get along, or they'll leave you behind!' Mike gave his mother a quick kiss, waved to his sister and aunt then hurried off in pursuit of Mrs Coleman, who had rejoined her boats.

'If I'm not mistaken,' said Auntie Peggy to her sister, 'that's a boy who doesn't seem too bothered about coming home just yet!'

'I've never seen anyone so happy,' said his mother, who had noticed a difference in her son. It was more than just his beaming face, the eager tone of his voice, or the colour of his healthy limbs. Was he more grown up than before? Did he seem rather distant, as if he didn't belong to her any more? She couldn't quite put her finger on it, but there was definitely a change in him, she thought.

'Well, at least the house will be quiet for a couple more days,' said Marilyn, though she secretly wished – now that her own holiday was over – that she could have joined her brother aboard those boats, just for a short while, to see what it was like. She wished, at least, that she could have had a quick peep into the little cabins.

The three of them stood a few moments longer, until the boats disappeared below the lock and away round the bend, then they turned and made their way home.

Back aboard *Cepheus* Mike was happy once again. He'd had a strange feeling as the boats reached his home town. It was the place where he'd spent all his life, yet, passing through on the waterway which skirted the town and which didn't quite belong to it, he felt that he didn't really belong there any more either. It was like being in a dream, where you find yourself in a familiar place and it seems real but you know it is not real. A place where you should be known but feel like a stranger. A place where nothing has changed, and yet everything has changed. Mike had felt no urgency to leave the boat and seek out his home, he was glad to be off again, happy to let the boats and the canal bear him away. He knew, of course, that it would only be for two more days and that he would have to go back. But he felt also that the canal was now his friend and that it would always be there waiting for him, to carry him away again with new companions, to new places – to a new life, if he wanted.

26. Fire!

The day grew sultry and humid. Irritating little black flies filled the air, and collected on Mike's shirt and face.

'Thunder flies,' remarked Mrs Coleman. 'There's gonna be a storm sooner or later, you wait an' see.'

'Let's just hope it holds off till we get these boats unloaded,' said Vince, gazing anxiously into the sky.

By mid-afternoon the boats were passing through one of those busy towns on the outskirts of London where, amongst the suburban houses, stood many modern factories and mills, some of which still relied upon the canal for their supplies of coal. Mr Coleman kept lifting his hat to mop his brow in the close heat, and everyone's clothing was sticking to their backs. The atmosphere was hazy and the sky had gone a funny sort of greenish-yellow colour, but still there was no rain.

Arriving at their destination around three o'clock, *Cepheus* and *Andromeda* were manoeuvred beneath the broad canopy of a large paper mill. Within half an hour their cargo of coal was being lifted out of the boats by a special grab on the mill wharf. By five-thirty both boats were empty and had been drawn away from the wharf to a quieter mooring place outside an adjacent warehouse. Here another, loaded pair of boats was already tied up.

'Are you gonna sweep out for me, Kit-an'-Mike?' asked Vince.

'We'll do it,' answered Kit.

'Only, I want to wash and change, 'cause I'm going out later,' his brother added. Vince, who had stripped to the waist, was sweaty and grimy after helping with the unloading. He had been shovelling the remnants of the coal into heaps large enough for the grab to pick up, and then he'd shovelled the very last of the heaps directly into the jaws of the grab. He looked weary.

The two younger lads willingly set to work after peeling off their shirts and began sweeping up the remains of the coal, mostly slack and dust. Theirs was the simplest job, but it was hard work in the exhausting heat. Perspiration ran down their faces, making little channels in the black dust that begrimed their foreheads and cheeks.

'I wonder what my dad would say if he could see me now,' said Mike. 'He'd think this was a very weird way to spend a holiday!'

'D'you mind?' said Kit. 'This is no 'oliday for me!'

'Oh, yeah. Sorry!' replied Mike. 'You know what I mean.' Then he asked, 'Don't you ever have holidays then?'

'We sometimes stay a couple of days with me gran and granddad. They've got a cottage near the cut, up by where we went through the tunnels. It's okay stayin' there for a bit, but I soon gets bored. I wanna be back on the boats again, moving on.'

Mike nodded sympathetically. He felt that he knew exactly what his friend was talking about.

At last their task was done, and they started to clean themselves up using a hose fixed to a tap that stood outside the doors of the warehouse. After trying unsuccessfully to keep their trousers dry, the two boys abandoned the attempt and began to squirt each other freely with the water. Playfulness developed into a full-scale battle and Mike and Kit ran to and fro, as jets of water spurted through the air and streamed all over the concrete pathway, until they were both thoroughly wet and hysterical with laughter.

Standing in the hatches, Mrs Coleman and Susannah watched the entertaining fight and laughed too, though they were occasionally splashed with stray squirts of water and had to duck as the two boys sent spray flying in all directions. In the sweltering heat of the evening the cool water was very welcome and refreshing – and at least it had rinsed away the grime and dust. The fun was also observed by a girl and a small boy on the adjacent boats; the girl had smiled and the boy had giggled and clapped his hands as Mike and Kit splashed around.

'It's our turn to have a night out in the town tonight, Kit,' Mrs Coleman announced at teatime. 'We 'aven't been to the pictures for a while, your dad and me, so we're goin' with Mr and Mrs Kingswell off the other boats. We're going to have ourselves a treat. You'll be all right here, won't you, the three of you? Only, don't go wandering off too far and leavin' the boats alone for long.'

It was too warm to be inside and they were all sitting in the hatches of the butty and on the cabin roof to eat their meal of cold bacon, salad and boiled potatoes.

'Where's our Vince goin', then?' asked Susannah.

'Oh, you know him,' said her mother. 'He's off to see his mate he found here once before – the lad who has the motorbikes. So you'll see him when you see him.'

'We'll find plenty to do,' said Kit. 'You go and 'ave a good time, Mum. You deserve it,' and he began to collect the plates and pans and signalled to Mike that it was time for them to start the washing-up.

They all waved goodbye to Kit's mum and dad (looking very handsome in their best outfits) when Mr and Mrs Kingswell came to meet them at seven o'clock. As they set off, Mrs Kingswell said, 'Our Barry and Virginia are on board, Kit. You'll look after them, won't you? I 'spect they'd enjoy playing some games with you all.'

Susannah said it was too hot to go out anywhere, away from the waterside, so the three of them settled down to entertain the two children from the other boats, making their own fun around the cluttered quayside by the warehouse. The concrete path where the boats were tied was not very deep, the walls of the building rising up only a short distance from the water's edge. But it was littered with oil drums, stacks of packing-cases and odd bits of machinery. An overhanging wooden awning gave some shade from the sun, so it was a perfect place to play. Virginia and Barry were coaxed from the cabin of the Kingswells' boats and were soon firm friends, joining in the games with enthusiasm.

Barry was about five, had a mop of blond hair and was dressed in a rather outsized pale-blue suit which had had several previous owners. Virginia was nearer Mike's age, about eleven, and was the sort of girl that adults like to call a 'tomboy'. She wore a dress and her hair was in a ponytail but she loved football and loved to be one of the boys when she had a chance. When she got dirty or grazed her knees and tore her frocks her mother despaired, but it didn't bother Virginia. So to start off the evening they had a session of goalie practice. There wasn't room to have a football game – and there were too few players anyway. But a steel gantry made an excellent goal and Virginia proved almost impossible to beat, no matter how the others tried. The ball had to be fished out of the cut about ten times and eventually they decided to play something else. Football was followed by 'Off-Ground Tig', using the objects scattered about the concrete path. This game was a great success because Barry loved to be chased and squealed with delight every time someone came running after him. His little legs could hardly move fast enough as he toddled here and there to escape capture. The game went on for ages until Barry was nearly pitched into the water. He clambered onto a wobbly pile of wooden palates and tipped them over. His sister rushed to grab him just in time, and then they thought it might be wise to stop. Instead they lay on the cabin tops of *Cepheus* and *Andromeda* in the stifling heat. They played a few games of 'I Spy', then Mike read to the others from his *Beano* comic, then they chatted together.

Virginia was quizzed about recent trips with her family's boats, and where they were going next. She was told all about Mike and how he came to be working with them. They related their adventures in Brummagem on Saturday night. Virginia hadn't seen *A Hard Day's Night* and was quite envious of the others. She made them tell her all about it, over and over. Then she decided that it was time for Barry to be put to bed, so she said goodbye to them all. With her little brother clasping her hand she wandered back to where her parents' boats were tied.

The others did not stir, but continued to enjoy the late evening warmth. There was no one else about. Though they could hear traffic not very far away this was a little oasis, cut off from the busy town nearby. The only link was a narrow passage, which ran between the high walls of the warehouse and a neighbouring workshop, and led to the street. The towing-path was on the other side of the canal, so there were no passers-by to disturb their peace.

'Your sister's very pretty,' said Susannah to Mike.

'S'pose so,' the boy replied – he'd never really considered whether Marilyn was attractive or not.

'Do you think she'd get on with our Joyce?'

'Your Joyce is a bit older than Marilyn,' Mike observed, 'but a lot more mature. I don't think Marilyn knows as much about life as Joyce. But . . .' he added, 'I'm sure they'd be great friends.'

'Has she got a boyfriend?' Susannah asked.

'She's had lots,' said Mike. 'I've lost count. But it's her girlfriends from school that she brings round to the house mostly.'

'It must be so easy for her to meet boys, and to see them when she wants,' Susannah said wistfully. 'Poor Joyce doesn't really know when she'll see her Roddy again. But, I s'pose it means she has to be faithful and they have to trust each other.' Susannah, though she was very young, was very thoughtful at times and liked to reflect on the strange twists and turns of life.

Kit, who hadn't really been listening, now said to Mike, 'Have you ever been to the seaside? We went once with one of our uncles when we were very small. It was only for the day and I'm not sure I liked it very much. There was too many people, crowds and crowds of 'em.'

'I've had lots of holidays by the seaside,' Mike said. 'We used to take a tent and go camping. It was really good fun. I enjoyed it. But – well, it's nice to have a change. I prefer moving around, anyway, and seeing different places every day.'

'Are you gonna miss us and the boats, Mike, when you go home?'

'You bet!' replied his friend with some feeling. 'I don't want to go home, and I don't want to go back to school. I'd much rather stay with you and go all the way to the docks, and then on another trip.' He paused for a moment, gazing into the distance, then added: 'I wouldn't mind staying on the boats always.'

'You can come back again,' said Kit, 'next year – or any time.'

'Anyway, I'm not going home just yet – I've got two more days!' Mike cried with glee. 'So I'm going to make the most of it!'

A few moments later Susannah said, 'Goodnight!' and slipped off the cabin roof into the hatches of the butty, and then into the cabin to bed. It was nearly ten o'clock.

'See you in the morning,' she called as she disappeared inside. She left the slide open and the doors ajar for it was far too hot to be closed in. In the last half-hour, however, a strong breeze had blown up and there were ripples on the water. The air was still humid and the darkening sky seemed leaden, a sickly green-grey colour.

'I s'pose we ought to get inside as well,' Kit said, 'or me mum and dad won't be very pleased if they finds us still up when they come 'ome.'

The two boys climbed into their cabin, but still didn't hurry to bed. Instead they sat on their bunks and continued to talk. It was too hot to sleep and they would only have lain awake in the stifling heat. They talked about cars. Kit didn't like them very much, and said he wasn't bothered about learning to drive. The only car he knew about was the Aston Martin – because he'd heard that 007 was going to have a special one in the new James Bond film. Mike said that was nothing, compared to the 'E' Type Jaguar. 'It's fab. It goes like a rocket and it's really stylish,' he crowed to his friend. But Kit didn't know enough or care enough about either car to argue, and their conversation lapsed into silence. Then Mike sniffed a couple of times and, wrinkling up his face in a puzzled look, asked, 'Can you smell something burning?' Kit realised then that there had been an acrid smell in the air for some time, but that he hadn't really taken any notice of it.

'I think something's on fire,' said Mike, leaping to his feet and clambering up the step to peep outside. What he saw made his heart leap and his legs went wobbly.

'This warehouse is on fire, Kit,' he shouted over his shoulder. 'Come and look!' Kit scrambled out of the cabin to join his friend and was amazed at the sight.

There was a line of sliding doors on the ground floor of the building, which opened onto the wharf. The top halves of the doors were glazed with dozens of small panes. Now, through these windows they could see a fierce fire raging inside. Its livid glow lit up their faces and the sides of the boats. Black smoke billowing up to the ceiling was beginning to seep out through gaps in the brickwork and between doors. Above their heads the awning was wreathed in smoke and they couldn't tell if the fire had spread to the floors above. Still, what they could see was frightening enough.

27. A Daring Rescue

For a moment neither boy could speak, then Kit said simply, 'What are we gonna do?'

'We ought to dial nine-nine-nine and get the fire brigade,' said Mike. 'But how do we get out?'

'There's a path down the side over there,' said Kit, pointing to where he had seen his parents disappear a few hours before.

'Shouldn't we get the others up and get them away from the boats?' said Mike.

'Okay,' said Kit. 'You go down the alley and see if you can find a phone box or a p'liceman or somethin', an' I'll get Susannah, and the kids off the other boats.'

They had a plan now. So Mike leapt from *Cepheus*, across the stern of the butty onto the wharf and immediately he could feel the heat from the burning building. The flames flickered more brightly through the glazed doors and smoke now billowed through the gaps between them. He ran quickly round the side of the warehouse to escape down the narrow passage. But turning the corner he saw to his horror that the fire was worse at the side of the building. It had already broken out through a door and several windows and was spread right across his path. As he stood dumbstruck, burning timbers collapsed in a cascade of sparks from one of the gaping, flaming openings, and tumbled into a crackling heap in the alley.

'It's blocked!' he shouted to Kit, running back to the boats on the concrete path. 'I can't get out – *WE* can't get out!' he stammered, really frightened now. Kit and Susannah stood like statues in the hatches of *Andromeda*, the roaring flames reflected in their eyes, and a look of utter fear on their faces.

'The fire's gonna burn through them doors in a minute,' said Kit, 'then we'll be for it.'

'Look!' shouted Susannah, pointing to the oil drums on which they had been playing a few hours before. 'Those barrels. Have they got petrol in, d'ya think, or chemicals or something dangerous?'

'Dunno,' said Mike, 'but they're going in the cut before the fire gets them. Come on, Kit!' And between them the two boys managed to roll eight heavy black drums one by one to the water's edge behind their moored boats. Each one was tipped into the cut where it bobbed about, close to the boats, but away from the heat of the flames.

'Someone must have seen the fire by now,' Mike said. 'Someone must have called the fire brigade. But we can't wait here for them to rescue us, we're just gonna get fried!'

'We'll 'ave to move the boats then,' said Kit.

'Can you start the engine?' Mike asked.

'I'm not sure,' Kit replied. 'I've only done it a few times and it's not very easy. We could just untie the boats and pull them out of the way I suppose.'

'But there's nowhere to take them to,' said Mike. 'There's no path past these buildings, we've got nothing to walk on to pull them along.'

'We'll use the long shaft an' push 'em out of the way, then,' said Kit. 'You go an' wake up Barry and Virginia, an' see if you can move their boats as well.'

While Mike hurried away Kit told Susannah to get back inside the cabin, away from the heat. He then loosed the boats from the rings at the fore-end and the stern and jumped down into the empty hold of the boat to pick up the long pole. It was heavy and cumbersome – and nearly three times as long as he was tall – and he struggled to lift it out of the hold. Standing on the fore-end he let the pole drop into the water and tried to push the boats along. Though detached from their moorings the boats were still tied together, side by side as a pair. They were heavy to move without the engine, and his pole sank deep into the soft bed of the canal, so Kit found he could hardly shift the boats any distance at all. The wind had got up, and was now quite strong, blowing the boats back onto the concrete wall at the canalside as fast as he could push them away. After several moments of muscle-wrenching effort he'd only moved the boats a few inches. He had to give it up. He was desperate now, and near to tears, he felt so helpless.

Mike came running back along the concrete path. 'I can't shift their boats at all,' he said. The Kingswells' boats were still loaded and the holds covered with sheets. 'They're too heavy and the wind's blowing against us.'

'I know. Same 'ere,' said Kit.

'I told Virginia to keep Barry inside for the moment,' Mike went on. 'It wouldn't be safe to let them out on the path.' After another minute, in which both boys looked helplessly at each other, Mike said, 'We could just swim for it, I suppose.'

'What, an' leave the boats to catch on fire?' said Kit. Mike looked rather ashamed as he realised what he had said, but thought they might have to do it anyway, unless they came up with another idea very soon.

'Well,' said Kit resolutely, 'I'll just have to 'ave a go at startin' the engine – or we're all gonna burn up.'

As he spoke there was a crashing sound and one of the pairs of sliding doors gave way. Flames that had been pent up in the warehouse now shot out with a terrifying roar. The boys had to jump back and run for cover aboard the boats. Kit dived into the engine hole, followed by Mike, who closed the doors behind him.

'Just give us a minute to try and remember what me dad does,' said Kit, flicking on the electric light and stooping over the inert engine. He thought for a bit, with a puzzled look on his face, and then began to turn a tap here and there, and to waggle a little lever to prime the engine. At that moment they heard a scream. Throwing open the engine-hole doors Mike could see Virginia's face above the cabin top of her boats. She was staring at the tarpaulin cloths over the hold, now exposed to the full heat of the blaze. It was beginning to smoke. 'We're gonna catch fire!' she shouted, desperately. Mike leapt across the butty onto the wharf and made a dash for the hose that they had been playing with earlier. With his back to the wall of the warehouse he was screened a little from the heat. He turned on the tap. The jet of water would be little use in fighting the blaze, but he played it along the side of Virginia's boat to soak the smouldering tarpaulin. Glancing over to the Colemans' boats he could see that the paintwork on the cabin side of *Andromeda* was beginning to blister, so he played the hose there too and ran the narrow jet back and forth along both boats. Then he had a thought and turned the hose on himself too – he decided that if his clothes were damp he would be less likely to catch fire himself when the time came to make a run for it.

'Wally!' shouted Kit from the depths of the engine hole. 'Come here a minute and give us a hand.' Virginia had leapt from her boats and Mike passed the hose to her, instructing her to keep the jet of water playing across the tarpaulins. He ran to join his friend on *Cepheus*.

'You've got to flick this thing over when I gets the engine turning fast enough,' Kit instructed, indicating a lever on the top of the engine case. 'I'll shout when I'm ready.' Mike dutifully held the lever and watched while Kit gripped a large crank-handle and began to turn, his whole body straining with the effort. He turned and turned, faster and faster, and then shouted to Mike, who quickly flicked the lever as he'd been instructed. It seemed like an eternity to both boys as they waited for the engine to show some sign of response. But nothing happened.

'You 'ave a go,' shouted Kit, 'my arms is aching.' With some difficulty in the confined space they exchanged positions and whilst Kit reset the lever Mike had a go at swinging over the engine. It was harder than he'd thought, but after several mighty turns he managed to gain speed and Kit pushed the lever over. There was a splutter, and a loud bang and the engine ran for several seconds, then died. The two boys stood looking at it in complete exhaustion and dejection.

'One more go, Kit,' said Mike, encouraging his friend. 'Don't let's give up!' And swapping places once more he gripped the lever whilst Kit swung the handle again for all he was worth. He thought a blood vessel was going to burst in his head, it was pounding so hard. The heat was terrific, his arms were burning with pain, but he swung the handle over and over before screaming 'NOW!' Mike slammed the lever across and the engine suddenly burst into life with a roar so deafening that for a moment they were rooted to the spot with surprise and shock.

'You've done it!' shouted Mike, hugging his friend. 'YOU'VE DONE IT!!'

'Now let's get away,' Kit replied, stumbling up the steps and falling out of the engine-room doors. 'We'll have to tie the Kingswells' boats on to ours. Can yer do that Mike, while I grab the tiller? I'll move as soon as you gimme the signal,' and he disappeared into the cabin in search of the polished brass tiller, which was always removed from its shaft when the boats were tied up.

Outside, the raging fire was rapidly overtaking everything around the boats. Having by this time burst through the doors it had flared upwards and caught the awning hanging over the wharf. Shards of burning asphalt and fragments of charred wood cascaded onto the boats in showers of sparks. Virginia had had to retire from the hose when the heat became too much for her. Instead she'd propped it in a cleft on an old weighing machine, and its jet still sprayed water across the wharf.

Then several things began to happen all at once, though in their desperation the two boys were only half-aware of them. From the distance came the frantic ringing of bells – the fire engines were on their way. Above this could be heard a deafening cracking and roaring sound, which shook the air around them. It was nothing to do with the fire. The long-threatened storm that had been expected all day was about to burst. The thunder rumbled, and above their heads spectacular blue-white flashes of lightning pierced the sky, for a split second illuminating everything around them as bright as daylight.

The two pairs of boats lay about fifteen feet apart and Mike was having difficulty getting a line tied between them. The heat was intense and he couldn't get near enough. Kit could see that his friend was in trouble so he made a dash for the hosepipe, grabbed it, and trained it onto Mike's body. Protected by the icy water Mike was able quickly to get the rope attached and then he waved frantically to Kit. 'Get on quick, let's go, let's go!' he shouted. Kit dropped the hose, but as he jumped across to the counter and revved the engine he could still feel water dropping onto his head and shoulders – it had begun to rain. Mike clambered along the gunwale to join his friend, and Kit steered the pair out from under the burning awning toward the centre of the canal. The other pair followed behind with Virginia crouching anxiously over her tiller in the hatches of the butty. Barry's frightened crying could be clearly heard above all the other din. 'I want my mum!' he wailed, over and over.

Slowly the boats inched away from danger, leaving the blazing building behind as Kit steered them along the canal and across to the towpath on the other side. The storm now broke with tremendous force, huge raindrops pelting heavily about them, roughing up the surface of the water and cooling their hot and aching bodies. Kit tipped his head back so that the chilly downpour beat into his face; he opened his dry mouth and the water tasted sweet on his tongue. He looked at Mike, and then the two boys hugged each other and laughed aloud with sheer exhilaration and relief. Next they heard the rasping sound of an engine being driven flat out, and roaring down the towpath came two lads on a large BSA motorbike, bouncing and skidding wildly on the pot-holed path. It was Vince's friend, with Vince himself seated behind.

'Are you lot okay?' screamed Vince, jumping off the pillion seat before the bike had stopped and almost stumbling into the canal. 'Good work, Kit-an'-Mike,' he said breathlessly as he rushed up to the two boys, and took hold of a line to pull the boats in to the side. 'Good work lads! We thought you was done for. Where's Susannah?'

'I'm here!' cried his sister from the stern of the butty, giving Vince a proud smile. 'Have you seen Mum and Dad?'

'They're comin' now,' said Vince, and sure enough through the pouring rain the silhouette of four figures could be seen hurrying across a bridge further down the canal. Without slackening their pace they came on, splashing along the uneven towpath till they reached the boats.

'Oh, thank heavens you're all right,' cried Mrs Coleman, almost in tears. There may even have been tears in her eyes, but they would not have been noticed, as water tumbled freely from the sky in raindrops 'like stair-rods' – as Mike's grandmother used to say. The rain drenched everything and everyone with its welcome coolness; even the fire across the cut seemed to have diminished a little in the deluge.

'– and you moved the boats too! You wonderful lads,' said Mr Coleman, who then found himself completely lost for words, and stood there dumbly looking at them. Without another word he grabbed each boy in turn, gave them an appreciative hug and ruffled his large hands through their hair. Meanwhile Mr and Mrs Kingswell had hurried to their boats to find Virginia and to console Barry who was still sobbing.

On the other side of the cut the blazing awning began to crumble and then to fall in a great fiery mass onto the wharf and into the water – just at the place where the boats had been tied only minutes before. There was a hissing sound and the water bubbled. It sounded to Mike like the noise the chips made when his mum put them into the hot oil on her kitchen stove – only louder and more frightening. They all stood in silence in the pouring rain, watching, hardly daring to imagine what might have happened if the boats had not been moved away.

Above the burning warehouse firemen appeared at the top of tall ladders directing powerful jets of water into the flames. Two policemen and an ambulance driver came trudging along the towpath. They were concerned about the children and insisted on leading them all away, across the bridge and down a lane to where an ambulance was waiting. There they were closely inspected for burns or other injuries, but apart from being very dirty and exhausted all of them were declared to be unharmed. Mike had never been involved with the police before, or in an accident of any kind. Now he had escaped from a fire and he was surrounded by police cars and emergency vehicles, with blue lights flashing in the rainy darkness. He couldn't help feeling that he was in an episode of *Z Cars*, the new crime series he'd watched on the telly.

By the time they had returned to the boats and had been given some well-sugared tea it was very late. The storm blew itself out, and in the cool night that followed the humid and stifling day the weary children were glad to fall into their warm beds at last. Across the cut the work of dousing the fire in the warehouse and making the remains of the building safe went on throughout the night – but none of the children heard a thing.

28. At the Depot

Just as on his first morning on the canal, Mike awoke the following day to the steady beat of the engine and realised that the boats were under way. He sat up and glanced across the cabin to find that Kit was still in bed too, sound asleep. Looking at his wristwatch, which he kept in the drawer, Mike was horrified to find that it was nearly nine o'clock. He put the watch to his ear to check that it was still working, but its steady ticking told him that he was not mistaken.

He threw off the covers and climbed up the step to where Vince was steering. 'Why didn't you give us a shout, Vince? We've overslept,' Mike said.

'We thought you an' Kit needed a lie-in today,' the older boy replied. 'You were pretty dead-beat when we turned in last night. Anyway, if you've only just woke up then you must have needed the sleep! Now you're up, though, how about a cup o' tea for the workers?' and he winked at Mike.

'I'll get the kettle on, then,' said the other boy, dropping back down into the cabin. As he dressed and prepared tea at the same time, Mike couldn't help feeling a bit cheated – he only had today and tomorrow left and he'd already slept away over three hours of it! Still, as the memory of last night's drama returned to him he wasn't surprised that he had needed so much rest.

The locks came steadily one after another on this stretch as the canal descended towards London. But for most of the morning they had what the boaters call 'a good road' – all the locks were ready for them. Mr Coleman was steering the butty for a change and Mrs Coleman was working the locks, so they were managing easily without the younger boys. Before long, steaming mugs of tea had been handed round and both Mike and Kit were standing on the gunwale of *Cepheus*. They chatted with Vince about the events of the previous evening whilst hungrily munching Marmite sandwiches. The two boys talked excitedly in between mouthfuls, each outdoing the other in lurid accounts of their terrifying ordeal. Vince had to keep slowing them down and making them speak one at a time till he had a clear picture of what had happened. Then it was his turn.

'We was worried sick,' he said. 'We got back to the ware'ouse about half past ten and couldn't get down the passage because it was a mass of flames. Someone had called the fire brigade and there was a crowd of people just hangin' around, gawping. The police got there first, then the fire engines, and then Mum and

Dad arrived with the Kingswells. We explained to the police and firemen that you was all at the back, on the boats, and that's when we found the other way round to the towpath, down a lane and across the bridge. We thought that if you was asleep, or overcome by the smoke, we would 'ave to swim across an' rescue you. Actually, until we saw you and the boats safe on the towpath side we was all dreadin' that you might have been burned. It was pretty scary, I can tell you.'

'Do they know how it started?' Mike asked.

'I dunno,' Vince replied, 'but the ware'ouse was full of paper and cardboard, apparently; went up like a tinderbox. When we said that you was at the back, on the boats, one copper said maybe you kids had broken in and had been playin' games and set it on fire. But we told them straight, we don't do things like that!'

'I think we probably saved them from having a worse disaster!' Kit spoke up, his pride severely wounded. He felt that he and Mike were the unsung heroes of the day. 'They were lucky that we pushed all their rotten old oil drums in the cut, away from the fire, or who knows what might have happened?'

'Oh well, it's "water under the bridge" now, as they say,' Vince sighed. 'We're stopping at the depot on the way down, anyhow, to get the boat checked over. The butty cabin's gonna need repainting on one side and there's all these scorch marks and burns on the roof too, where burning stuff fell on it. Me Dad's a bit worried in case the heat has warped the sides of the butty – only we've managed to get through the locks okay, so I don't think there's any real 'arm done.'

Kit had gone quiet, thinking over something that Vince had just said. Then he spoke. 'It should be "water through the lock" really, shouldn't it? Not "water under the bridge"?' The other two just stared at him, then smiled at each other, as if to say, 'Barmy!'

The depot where they were to stop lay at a junction. Here the canal continued in two directions – both leading to dockyards on the Thames. So this was a busy and important place where pairs of boats were tied up waiting for orders or repairs. There was an office here, where the boat captains received their wages. And there were fuel pumps, and a store in the yard, which kept ropes and tarpaulins, planks and stove chimneys and all manner of equipment needed on the boats. As *Cepheus* and *Andromeda* drew in a grim-looking old man was standing on the concrete path watching them. Mike and Kit jumped off to tie up the boats, and as they leapt ashore the old man shouted to them, 'The police are after you two!' Because the man had such an old and weather-beaten face, a face shaded by the broad flat cap that he wore, neither of them could see his eyes twinkling and the faint smile on his lips. They only heard his tired old voice and the words uttered in a flat and expressionless way. So their immediate thought was that they were in serious trouble. Mike and Kit looked at each other.

'We 'aven't done nothing wrong,' they began to protest to the man. 'Do they still think we started that fire last night, then?'

'Better go and see!' was all that the old fellow would say. 'They're up at the office,' and he jerked his head to one side, indicating the solitary shed that stood some distance away from the waterside.

Mike and Kit agreed that if there had been a misunderstanding, or if they had been falsely accused, they had better get the matter sorted out straight away. With a quick shout to Mr Coleman, and pointing vaguely in the direction of the office, the two boys hurried off.

With their hearts beating fast and mouths feeling rather dry they pushed open the door to face their accusers. As they entered the small cabin which answered for an office, a sea of faces met their anxious stares. In the crowded room there were two uniformed policemen; a man whom Kit recognised as Mr Richards, the clerk who usually issued orders, behind the desk; his secretary; and two other men in shirtsleeves, one of whom carried a notepad, the other a camera.

'Here they are themselves, then,' said Mr Richards. 'Now, lads, we've been expecting you. What have you been up to, eh?' and he looked at them sternly.

'We never done nothing,' Kit began, sounding a little agitated.

'All we did was try to stop the fire spreading, and get the boats out of the way,' Mike added, quietly.

'Steady on, steady on. Let's get you one at a time,' said the first police officer, and he pulled out his report book. 'What we want is a statement, so that we can make a full report on the incident. And then we have to pass on to you the thanks of the warehouseman for your sensible actions.' Mr Richards was smiling now, and the two boys relaxed a little, the tension disappearing from their faces. They were still unsure whether they were supposed to have done right or wrong, whether they were being praised or ticked off, but before they could ask any questions themselves the other officer spoke.

'Right, lads. In your own words, tell us what happened from the moment you discovered the fire. And by the way, these gentlemen' – he pointed to Camera and Notepad – 'are from the papers, and they want to get your story as well – and a photograph.'

The boys were dumbstruck. It began to dawn upon them that they really weren't in trouble. In fact it looked as if they were heroes after all – just as Kit had believed.

Carefully they went over every action of the incident, from the moment when Mike had smelled something burning, to their escape across the water. As the policeman made notes, so one of the shirt-sleeved men scribbled away too. He spoke up now and then, asking the boys for more details like 'got any brothers and sisters, lads?' until the police officer frowned at him and told him not to interrupt. When the constable was satisfied that he had all the information he needed he congratulated the two boys and said that the warehouseman was very grateful for what they had done, and that – possibly – there might be a little reward coming their way. And he tapped the side of his nose with his forefinger in a knowing sort of way. Then he tucked his report book back in his pocket and, bidding them all good morning, departed with his companion.

The door had hardly closed on the two officers before Camera and his mate pounced on the boys.

'Okay lads, now what we want is a good photo of you by your boats,' said the first man.

'Hold on a minute!' interjected Notepad. 'I just want a few more details first, if you don't mind, boys; about your families, and about your work on the boats.' When the final question had been answered to the journalist's satisfaction he said, 'And now I have to think of a good headline, saying as how you two saved the lives of the little kiddies, as well as rescuing the boats and chucking the oil drums into the water.'

Mike reflected that Virginia and Susannah would not appreciate being referred to as 'the little kiddies', but his head was swimming by this time, excited as he was at the prospect of being in the papers.

Leaving Mr Richards to restore normal service in his office they all walked down to the waterside together and several photographs were taken of Kit and Mike posing near the boats. Then the reporters hurried away to write up the story in time for the evening editions.

'You'd better give your mum a call, Mike,' said Mrs Coleman. 'If she reads about your lucky escape in the paper before you tell her what happened she might get a bit of a shock!' So Mike, accompanied by Kit, hurried away to find a phone box. As they disappeared Mrs Coleman winked to Susannah, who winked back, and both of them fell to furtive activity in the butty cabin.

When the two boys returned neither of them suspected there was a plot to keep them out of the way. Mr Coleman grabbed them immediately and put them to work touching up some of the blistered paintwork on *Andromeda*, and they were happy to oblige. He kept them busy for the rest of the afternoon fetching and carrying. New ropes were issued at the store to replace the charred ones, and workmen brought new tarpaulin sheets to be fitted along the side of the boat which had been nearest to the fire. Though they had been rolled up, the old ones had been badly scorched by the heat, and were full of holes.

At four o'clock Mrs Coleman sent Mike, Kit and Susannah off with eightpence to buy the evening paper – two copies, so that Mike could have one to keep. The children were eager to get to the shop and could hardly wait to see what had been written about them and the fire. Rushing out of the shop and spreading out a copy of the *Evening News and Star* on a nearby bench, the children's excitement grew. Sure enough there was a big headline and photographs – though not on the front page. They had to turn to page five for the story, but they were not disappointed. In tall, bold letters ran the line 'BRAVE BARGE BOYS' and in smaller, bold letters beneath it said: 'Boats and Young Children Saved From Fierce Fire by Prompt Action'. There were two photographs, one showing the two boys with Susannah standing in front of the scarred cabin side of *Andromeda* and a second, smaller picture of the remains of the warehouse, taken that morning.

'We're not "Barge Boys"'! was Kit's first, indignant remark. 'People always call our boats barges, an' they're *not*. They're narrow boats – but never mind,' he sighed wearily, and shrugged his shoulders.

'It's a smaller word,' Mike suggested. 'Perhaps they couldn't fit "Brave Narrow Boat Boys" onto the page!'

'Read what it says!' Susannah interrupted, impatient to hear the story. She was on tiptoe, looking over the boys' shoulders, and couldn't see the text.

'Christopher Coleman (13) and Michael Walker (12) didn't hesitate in the face of danger yesterday . . .' Mike began to read aloud. Only parts of the story seemed recognisable from their own account of what happened, and it was obvious that the press men had done their stuff. But there were no actual untruths in it, and the children were quite impressed and pleased with the dramatic way in which their tale had been retold.

'Toddler Barry Kingswell, asleep in the cabin of the adjacent boat, would certainly have perished if it had not been for the two lads . . .'; 'Lethal drums of inflammable liquid were quickly despatched by the boys, who rolled them out of harm's way into the canal . . .'; 'In the absence of the parents the boys remained cool and rational . . .'; 'All four barges were drawn away from the fire and suffered only minor damage . . .'; 'situation could have been very grave indeed . . .'; 'the children were exhausted and frightened, but physically unharmed . . .'

'Coo!' said Susannah, as Mike finished reading, and Kit gave a whistle – which expressed his satisfaction with the article. Mike had a far-away look in his eyes.

'Fame!' he said, slapping Kit on the back. 'Wait till all my mates at school hear about this!'

'And I'll be talked about all along the cut!' said Kit, with a laugh. 'Everyone'll want my autograph, just like a pop star!'

'I think we were all really lucky,' said Susannah, solemnly. 'I know you did the right thing, an' you saved the boats as well, but we could have been hurt. What if that building had fallen on us, or what if . . .' But Kit cut her off short.

'What if what, Sue? Come on, it's all over now, let's forget about it. We've got our pictures in the paper, and you don't get that every day of the week – you 'ave to let us 'ave our little bit of glory! Let's go back 'ome now.'

Back at the boats the children found a special surprise awaiting them – or at least Mike and Kit did, because Susannah had been in on the secret and had helped her mother with the preparations. Virginia and Barry were there looking very excited. Their boats had been unloaded at the wharf that morning and the Kingswells had then followed the Colemans down the cut. They were now tied up nearby. Barry was wearing a cowboy outfit which his mum had bought to cheer him up, and he was running around happily again, full of laughter, his ordeal of the previous night apparently forgotten. He and his sister had been waiting eagerly for their friends to return from the shop. 'Come an' look at this!' Virginia shouted, and Barry fired off a couple of shots from his cap-gun as he and his sister led the others towards *Andromeda*.

There, spread about the cabin roof, was a feast of lovely things to eat. There were fat sausage rolls piled up like a stack of logs, chocolate biscuits in many shapes and sizes, crisps in bowls and a garish green jelly. There were lemon tarts, freshly baked, and sugar-topped cream puffs from the bakers. There were ham, egg and corned-beef sandwiches, and a trifle and savoury cheese straws. And in the centre was the fruit cake which Mike's mum had made, only Mrs Coleman had now iced it, and on the top – with Susannah's help – she had placed a little model of a narrow boat, made out of marzipan and rather curiously coloured with food dyes.

'Surprise!' cried Mrs Coleman. And Susannah, Virginia and Barry, jumping up and down, joined in, shouting 'Surprise, surprise!'

'Cor!' and 'Wow!' were the only words the boys could find as their eyes lit up at the sight.

'Tuck in!' invited Mrs Coleman. 'This is a special "Thank You" treat for you two, for all you did yesterday. And it's a sort of "Farewell Tea" for our Mike too, 'cause he's leaving us tomorrow.'

As all the children dived into the plates of goodies Mrs Coleman read the story in the paper, uttering occasional 'Mmms' and 'Ahs' of approval, and admiring the photograph.

'Proper little stars, both of you,' she said, turning to Mike and Kit.

'Oh, don't get them goin' again, Mum,' sighed Susannah, 'their 'eads are big enough already!' The boys – all sticky-fingered and cream-dotted around their faces – made no reply. They were too busy disposing of large quantities of food, eager to try something from every plate.

'Leave some for our Vince,' urged Mrs Coleman. But it was such a vast spread that, although Mike and Kit tried their best, with the others' help, there was still plenty left even when they were all quite full.

One or two people from other pairs of boats wandered along to the little party. From somewhere aboard Mr Coleman dug out an old wind-up gramophone, and its jazzy music attracted more friends to join in the fun. Mrs Coleman was kept busy making tea, and other young children were invited to tuck into the food, so that there was soon a cheerful gathering of boat people and a happy buzz of conversation around the Colemans' boats. Much of the talk was about the fire, of course, and Mrs Coleman was obliged to read out the newspaper story several times for the benefit of the other adults. Mike and Kit – enjoying the attention – were called upon to retell their adventures, whilst Susannah and Virginia – determined not to be overlooked – supplied a lively account of their own part in the action.

Everyone seemed to know that Mike was shortly to leave the boats. Several people shook his hand or slapped him on the back and said things like, 'You won't wanna stay on the bank now you've been on the boats, Mike – we'll expect you back soon!' Or, 'We could do with a few more youngsters like you on the cut, Mike. Fancy comin' to be a steerer with us?' Though he could happily have spent many more days with the Colemans – and put off the moment when he had to report to his new school – Mike knew he had to leave. But these comments and compliments, which he knew were genuine, increased his feeling of warmth towards the canal folk he had come to know just a little in the last fortnight. At the same time they made his heart feel all the heavier for having to leave them and his new-found life on the water.

As the afternoon became evening, so people began to drift away and Mike exchanged many farewells with people he hardly knew, though he felt he had known them all his life. The depot fell quiet, and the storesmen and office staff began to make their way home. One or two pairs of boats passed by, heading northwards, ready for an early start ahead of everyone else the next day.

'We're off to the docks in the morning!' shouted Vince, who now came running back to the mooring clutching a slip of paper. 'Timber for Brummagem!'

29. Last Day

A strong wind was blowing across the cut the following morning, curling tiny waves over the surface of the water. It would be September in a few days' time and though the sun shone brightly in a high blue sky there was a nip in the air, hinting that summer might at last be giving way to autumn. *Cepheus* and *Andromeda* were under way once more, after leaving the depot early. The inspection at the yard had shown that there was no damage to the hull of *Andromeda* and it had been arranged for the paintwork to be properly re-done later in the year. So everything was 'back to normal' for the Colemans and a new trip had begun with the boats bound for the docks down by the Thames to load with timber.

Kit had made coffee and sandwiches for elevenses, and now Mike was in the cabin, stuffing his clothing and his few possessions back into his holdall. Mid-afternoon would bring them to the place where Kit's mum had said he could get to the railway station easily, so he wanted to be ready to jump off when the time came, and to delay the boats as little as possible.

With the remains of his pocket money he had bought a small box of chocolates the day before, as a present for Mrs Coleman, and with Vince's help he had purchased a packet of cigarettes for Mr Coleman. He looked at these presents now, lying there on his bed. He had no fancy paper to wrap them in, but he decided that they would be just as acceptable presented in brown paper bags. With only a few pennies left now, apart from the money his mother had left for his train fare, he was puzzled about what to give to the others, especially Kit. Mike sat on his bunk, his chin propped in his hands, whilst he considered this. Then he made up his mind that he would leave his friend his Swiss Army penknife. Kit had admired it lots of times, and he knew that his dad would understand if he returned home without it. It pleased him a great deal to think that he was giving something he valued to his friend, and he knew that Kit would realise how special this gift was.

To Susannah he would give his bird book. He had others at home, and he knew that she would enjoy practising her reading with it, and he'd noticed how she liked to look out for the different birds along the cut. Which left only Vince. What could he give to him? Then he had a brainwave, and as the idea came to him a smile of satisfaction broke out on his face. He jumped to his feet. Everything was organised now, so he could go back up to the cabin-side and enjoy the last few hours that remained of his adventure.

As he stepped out Mr Coleman handed him the tiller. 'You'd better get a bit more practice in, Mikey. Don't know how long it'll be before you gets the chance again.' As Mike settled himself into the doorway to steer, Kit stood on the gunwale and the two friends chatted together and watched the scenery go by. The straight water-channel stretched ahead to the horizon and Mike secretly hoped that it would never end.

The boats were nearing the centre of London. There were no locks now, but there were many large and busy factories that towered over the canal. Mike had spotted several familiar names beside the cut in recent days, like Ovaltine and Nestles, whose products he knew. Now here was a well-known jam factory, with boats unloading coal up a short arm.

The waterway crossed a broad highway busy with traffic and wound beneath wide railway bridges where frequent trains thundered and clattered past, the deafening roar obliterating the sound of their engine. In the shade beneath the bridges the air was momentarily chill. Occasionally they met huge wide barges, many of them filled with rubbish destined for the tip. They passed a sprawling railway yard where dirty black engines stood outside sheds, wreathed in smoke and steam, waiting to begin their duties. Later, a cluster of vast gas-holders loomed up on one side of the cut, and on the opposite bank a derelict cemetery. Behind rusting ornamental railings sun-blanched gravestones protruded like old teeth from the rampant vegetation that spread about the tombs and broken columns.

'Nearly there now, Mikey,' Mr Coleman said to him, softly. 'Are you all set to go, mate?' Mike gave up the tiller and dived into the cabin. He paused and took one last lingering look around the tiny, cosy little space which had been his home for nearly two weeks. There was the brightly painted castle on the cupboard door, worn and scratched and patched up countless times. On the wall a calendar and the cut-out photos of motorbikes and the Beatles. The battered old kettle with which he had made dozens of drinks stood on the shiny hob of the black iron stove. Brass rails and knobs glittered, and the lace doily in the porthole window quivered with the vibration from the engine. Kit and Vince's clothes were scattered on their bed, and a couple of plates and mugs, which had escaped the washing-up, were perched on a shelf. An odd mixture of tools and fire-irons, stray lumps of coal, Vince's Airfix motorbike models, a tin of Brasso, books, a transistor radio, a bicycle pump and an odd shoe were scattered about or stuffed into the many little pigeonholes and shelves around the cabin. Mike's glance noted all these familiar things in a moment and imprinted the scene on his memory.

Then he grabbed his bag, sprang back onto the deck and said, with a lump in his throat, 'I'm ready.' He shook Mr Coleman's free hand, presented him with the cigarettes and thanked him for all he had learned on the boats. Mr Coleman said, 'You needn't have done that, Mikey, but thanks very much,' and he added, 'You'll be a steerer yet, lad! Don't think you've seen the last of the boats – or us!' He then steered Cepheus towards the towpath and brought the boat to a standstill. Mike jumped off, and ran back to the butty where Mrs Coleman stood on the path, holding Andromeda on a line. Mike gave her the chocolates and thanked her for looking after him. The woman seemed quite moved and she hugged him and said, 'Come back soon, love!' and then pointed out the way to the station.

Susannah was looking a little sad, so Mike bent down and kissed her, then slipped the bird book into her hands. The little girl's face broke out in a broad smile and she reached up as high as she could to hug Mike round his middle. Then he said to Vince, 'Sorry, I haven't managed to get a present for you, Vince. But I thought that, if you want, any time you go past where I live, you can come to the Speedway with me and my dad – and he can drive you back to the boats afterwards.' Vince was more than happy with this promise of a present, and he gripped Mike's hand firmly as he said, 'Goodbye, Mikey. It's not gonna be the same without you around, man. Look after yourself!'

'And this is for you, Kit,' Mike said, turning finally to his friend. He dipped his hand into his pocket and produced the penknife. 'You can't gimme that!' Kit protested. 'It's your own special knife!' But Mike insisted, 'I want you to have it. I know you'll take care of it and make use of it – perhaps it will come in handy when you're splicing.' Kit was speechless, and stood gazing at the gift as he turned it over in his hands, the bright steel of the blade-backs catching the sunlight. In the brief silence that followed Mike seized his opportunity, said one more goodbye to them all and started away along the path. But before he'd taken many steps he stopped, turned and trotted back.

'I nearly forgot,' he said, and reaching behind him he pulled out his windlass from his belt where, through habit, it was still tucked. He held it out to Mr Coleman.

'You'd better have this back.'

'No, no!' said Kit's father, pushing it firmly back into Mike's hands. 'That's your iron now, Mikey, my lad. You've worked hard for that, and you've earned it. You 'ang on to it and keep it safe – you'll need it ready for the next time you come on the boats.'

'Aw, thanks very much!' said Mike, his face lighting up. He was delighted and proud to be taking home such a prize, and hurriedly fixed it back in his belt.

At home the windlass would be hung on the wall above his bed. Either side of it Mike would place a painting – one of *Cepheus*, one of *Andromeda* – pictures he would paint himself in the autumn when the nights drew in and rain or fog gripped the landscape so that he couldn't go out of doors. And above the windlass and the paintings, in a frame that his mother would get specially for him, would be the photograph of Mike with his friends on the boats, caught in one happy moment of those wonderful days when he had spent his summer on the cut.

30. Summer's End

Mike dashed away from the boats and up the sloping path that led to the main road going over the bridge. At the top he turned to find that the boats were already moving onwards. He leaned over the parapet and gave them one final wave as they passed beneath and out of sight, on towards the docks, for another load, and another trip on their unending journey. Mike suddenly felt very lonely as he stood there amidst the noisy and bewildering London traffic – the cars and vans and big red buses, and cyclists darting in and out of the moving vehicles. Slowly he began to thread his way through the busy thoroughfare where huge advertisement hoardings and illuminated signs vied for his attention.

Hundreds of people passed him on the pavement, and no one gave him a second glance. Many of them had their heads down, intent only on what they had to do and where they were going. He found the station, bought his ticket and was glad to stand in the shade of the station awning for a while as he waited for his train.

When it arrived the rake of maroon coaches squealed to a halt at the platform and Mike ran along from door to door looking for a spare seat. Because it was not yet the 'rush hour' the carriages were not very crowded and he managed to find a compartment to himself. He pulled the window right down so that he could lean out and feel the wind in his face and in his hair as the train gathered speed. Everything whizzed past so fast as the train rocked and swayed along, it was almost frightening. Here and there beside the railway line or between gaps in the houses and factories he caught glimpses of the canal, which followed the same route as the railway for many miles and sparkled brightly in the afternoon sun. He even spotted a pair of boats placidly chugging along, but they were gone in an instant before he had time to wave. Within forty-five minutes the train had reached his station. Mike reflected that he had just covered the same distance that the boats had taken two days to travel.

He gave up his ticket, left the station and started across town towards his home, his holdall slung over his shoulder. As he strode along it seemed strange to Mike not to be near water. All about him he saw not rough grassy paths and the cut stretching away in front and behind, but tarmac and paving stones which looked so dead and static. Once, these familiar streets had made him feel secure and comfortable. Now he knew that another world, another life, lay beyond the neat houses with their net curtains and carefully tended gardens. And he knew that one day he would leave them again. On this day, though, they seemed friendly enough, and they welcomed him and he realised that, yes, he had missed them a bit after all – though in his big boots and scruffy old clothes he felt very self-conscious as he passed by. He was looking forward to seeing his mum and dad again – and Marilyn. He had so much to tell them all, and his pace quickened as he thought how pleasant it was to be home again. He even admitted to himself that it would be nice to sit down in front of the telly, and to be back in his own little bedroom with all its familiar things.

Then, turning the corner into his street he bumped straight into a boy who was running along the pavement. It was his friend Andy.

'Hey! Wally Walker!' the boy cried, surprised but pleased to see his schoolmate.

'Where've you been?'

'On my holidays,' said Mike. 'Just got back now.' Andy turned in his tracks to accompany his friend and the two boys walked along amiably together.

'We went camping,' Andy said, 'by the seaside, Great Yarmouth – had a fantastic time. And it was sunny for nearly the whole fortnight. You've got a really good tan too, have you been by the sea?'

'Nope!' said Mike, proffering no further information.

'Where did you go, then?' asked the other lad eagerly. 'Somewhere exciting?'

'You'll never believe me!' said Mike, with a laugh. 'You'll never believe me!' They were at his gate now, and he smiled at his puzzled friend and skipped up the path. 'Tell you later!' he shouted, and hammered the knocker on the door.

THE END

Finding out more about the life of the Waterways

Books

There are no books written by actual members of old boating families, but other people who have worked on the canals have recorded observations of the way of life of the boat people. First amongst these are women who worked on the Grand Union Canal during the Second World War and afterwards wrote about their experiences:

Idle Women – by Susan Woolfitt
Maiden's Trip – by Emma Smith
Troubled Waters – by Margaret Cornish
The Amateur Boatwomen – by Eily Gayford

In the 1950s and 60s many young men discovered the special way of life of the canals and some spent several years working on narrow boats. The recollections of two of these men may be found in:

Anderton for Orders – by Tom Foxon
Bread Upon the Waters – by David Blagrove

All the above books are now published by Mark Baldwin of Cleobury Mortimer. In addition Tom Foxon's second book, *Number One*, is published by J. M. Pearson & Son of Burton upon Trent.
John Thorpe has written of his teenage experiences working on narrow boats in the 1950s in the book *Windlass in My Belt*, published by Waterways World.
There are many other books on canals, about their history, the craft that traded on them, the engineers who built them, and about architectural or engineering features of the waterways. Look in your local library for these.

Museums and Societies

An exciting way to learn more about the boats and the way of life of the boat people is to visit one of the National Waterways Museums at:

Gloucester
Llanthony Warehouse, Gloucester Docks, Gloucester, GL1 2EH
☎ 01452 318200; www.nwm.org.uk
Gloucester has a Society of Friends which supports the museum with volunteer activities.

Ellesmere Port (formerly the Boat Museum)
South Pier Road, Ellesmere Port, Cheshire, CH65 4SW; ☎ 0151 355 5017; www.boatmuseum.org.uk
The Boat Museum Society supports the museum with a wide range of volunteer work and activities; it also owns and runs two traditional canal boats.

Stoke Bruerne, Northamptonshire (canalside at lock 14); ☎ 01604 862229
There is a group of Friends of the Museum at Stoke.

All three sites have examples of boats and artefacts from the canals as well as engaging exhibitions and displays. Look them up, and their support groups, on their websites or on www.thewaterwaystrust.org.uk

If you would like to get involved in caring for and operating traditional narrow boats, have a look at the following societies:

The Working Boats Project (working with the BW Heritage Fleet)
The Narrow Boat Trust (caring for and working a pair of Grand Union boats, often with a load)
The Horse Boating Society (maintaining the traditional skills of horse-drawn boating)
The Boat Museum Society (mentioned above; aims to operate boats around the system, at rallies and shows, as a visible reminder of traditional boating techniques)

Glossary

Some words and things in the story that might need further explanation.

Measurements

Before we began to conform with European metric measurements, the British Imperial system used inches, feet and yards.
One foot equals 12 inches; three feet make a yard.

   1 inch = approximately 2.54cm
   1 foot = approximately 30.48cm
   1 yard = approximately 91.44cm

Money

Before British coinage went decimal in the early 1970s we had a system of POUNDS, SHILLINGS and PENCE, or £. s. d., and some of the coins had popular nicknames.

The pound was divided into twenty shillings (20/-). Each shilling was worth twelve pennies (12d). The various coins were: pennies and halfpennies (ha'pennies); the threepenny bit (or 'joey'), the sixpenny piece (or 'tanner'), the shilling (or 'bob'), the two shilling piece (also called a florin), and the half-crown, worth two shillings and sixpence (2/6d) – there were eight of these to the pound. There was a brown banknote worth ten shillings (10/-), and a green one-pound note. Larger banknotes existed but were rarely seen in daily life, being much more valuable than now – five or ten pounds was a huge sum of money.

Don't try to convert old money into new on face value, because actual values are quite different. For example, my pocket money when I was twelve or thirteen in the 1960s was a very generous half-a-crown. Today this would be 12½p! But my two-and-six would buy me lots of things – a Mars bar cost just sixpence. My dad's wages were about £15 a week, and he was well paid. In Chapter 18 Vince buys cinema tickets for two 'bob' each. This converts to '10p' today, but think what tickets cost now and you'll have some idea how values have changed.

Balance Beam	The long, heavy beam on a lock gate which acts as a lever for working the gate and as a counterbalance, making it easy to move.
Blades	The boatman's name for the boat's propeller (or 'prop').
Bow-hauling	The technique of pulling a boat (usually the butty, when detached from the motor) on a long rope attached to its mast. 'Bow' is pronounced the same as in 'bow tie.' In the days of river navigation boats would be hauled by teams of men on the bank, and loops or bows were often tied in the rope to make it easier to hold on.
Bridge 'ole	Boater's name for a bridge – the 'hole' or arch being the most important part from the boater's point of view.
Brylcreem	Still available today, this hair-styling cream was extremely popular in the 1940s, '50s and '60s, and was usually generously applied so that men's hair looked slick and shiny.
Bubblegum	A fruit-flavoured chewing gum which, if you were clever enough, could be blown into large bubbles. However, this wasn't considered a polite practice.
Bus Conductress	Today passengers buy tickets from the driver on entering a bus. In the 1960s there were conductors in addition to the driver, who sold tickets at your seat and thus allowed the bus to keep moving. They also kept order on the bus and would **kick off** troublemakers. A woman in this job was called a conductress.

Butlins	The holiday camp enjoyed its greatest popularity after the Second World War, when people flocked to Pontins and Butlins in vast numbers. The camps were very different from those which still operate today; accommodation was very basic and entertainment rather tame by modern standards.
Cratch	Roughly the first six feet of the cargo hold at the fore-end of a narrow boat, almost always clothed-in. The space beneath was generally used for storing the large top-cloths, various ropes or lines when not in use, and other articles.
Cross-bed	The fold-down double bed at the rear of the cabin which, when opened, lies across the width of the boat.
Door 'oles	The space within the pair of doors leading into the cabin, where the steerer stands.
Eagle	A weekly comic published from 1950 until 1969, which was popular amongst other things for its technical drawings of aircraft and motor cars and coverage of scientific subjects. It included the adventures of such famous characters as PC 49 and Dan Dare, the futuristic astronaut.
Elms	Once one of the most common trees in England before Dutch Elm Disease destroyed many of them in the 1970s. Their distinctive tall, billowing shapes were a familiar sight along country lanes and field margins. They are now very rare.
Elum	The boater's name (from the nautical word 'helm') for the wooden rudder of a butty boat or horse boat.
Engine 'ole	Boater's name for the engine room of a motor.
Furlong	You will be familiar with miles, because road distances are still measured in them. Furlongs are practically an obsolete measurement now, but they were used in calculating canal distances. One furlong = 220 yards, and there are 1,760 yards in a mile. Therefore eight furlongs make a mile.
Gasworks	Before North Sea Gas was piped ashore to the whole country in the 1970s, every town had its gasworks producing gas from coal. They had a distinctive smell, and were usually in the shabbier, run-down part of town.
Gramophone	A clockwork or electric machine for playing records (the old 78rpm ones), the predecessor of the Record Player. Though old-fashioned by the 1960s, many people still had them, and portable ones were handy to use on picnics or in the garden.
Gunwale	Pronounced (and sometimes spelt) 'gunnel'. The upper edge of the hull of any boat or ship, and on a narrow boat the foot-ledge that runs alongside the cabin (on motors) and along the cargo hold to the fore-end.
Hatches	The well-like space in the stern of a butty boat, where the steerer stands.
Legging	The process of working a boat through a tunnel by 'walking' along the sides whilst lying on a plank layed across the boat.
Lengthsman	(sometimes 'Lengthman') The canal employee charged with looking after a length of canal, which might be several miles. He would look out for damage and wear and tear. He usually occupied a cottage beside the canal, which might be totally isolated in some areas, and often only accessible by water.
Lino	Short for Linoleum, once a common floor covering before the introduction of vinyl floors and wall-to-wall carpeting. It was very hard and durable, and on winter's days very cold to bare feet.
Locks	Built in varying lengths on different waterways, but on Midlands canals usually accommodating boats of 70ft length, locks are the means of raising and lowering boats where the canal changes level. This ingenious device allowed the canal

system to spread all over the country. Locks are either single or double width, and sometime occur in pairs (side by side) on busy stretches of waterway.

Navvy, Navigation   Early canals were popularly known as Navigations, and the men who worked in huge gangs to build them were called Navigators or 'Navvies'. The word was later applied to men who built the railways, and today to those who work on our roads.

Narrow Boats, Motors, Butties and Barges   Narrow boats are generally about 70ft long and 7ft wide. The powered ones are known as motors, and would often tow an unpowered 'butty'. The butty was built in the same style as the original horse-drawn boats of the canals. These boats (also known as 'Long boats' or 'Monkey boats' in different areas) are often wrongly called barges. Barges are wider than 7 feet, usually 14 or 16 feet, and the men who steered them were called Lightermen.

National Service   After the Second World War had ended the government continued to conscript young men for military service. They spent two years in the army, navy or air force, and formed a reserve in case war should break out again. The scheme ended in 1960.

Paddles   The underwater sluices at the top and bottom ends of locks, some within the brickwork of the lock, others in the gates. They control the flow of water into and out of the lock and are operated by turning a windlass on gears mounted by the lock-side or on the gates.

Pictures   Popular name for the cinema (also known as 'The Flicks,' and, derogatively, 'The Flea Pit' – some cinemas were very shabby and ill-kept, and a good place to pick up bugs or germs!). In the old form of film classification a 'U' certificate meant unrestricted viewing, and the film could be seen by all ages, even unaccompanied children. At the other end of the scale was the 'X' certificate – only those over 18 were admitted.

Plimsolls   Young people like to wear expensive and stylish training shoes today – usually for fashion rather than sport. In the 1960s you wore plimsolls for PE at school, and sometimes as a light casual shoe at home or in the school holidays – or if you were poor you even wore them to school. They were cheaply made of canvas, with thin rubber soles, had laces or elastic sides and were available in black or white! Various local names existed for them; we called them 'pumps'.

Pound   A stretch of uninterrupted water between two locks, which might be only a few yards long or several miles.

Ranger 7   Launched by the United States in July 1964 as one of a series of moon-probes, Ranger 7 successfully returned 4,316 TV pictures of the Moon's surface showing features in great detail – a hundred times better than anything previously seen through Earth-based telescopes. The photographs were crucial in locating a suitable landing site for the Apollo craft that would put men on the moon in 1969.

Record Player   An electrical machine for playing vinyl records, at either 45 or 33rpm. Every young person in the '60s wanted a record player so that they could listen to 'singles' of their favourite pop groups and singers. Marilyn probably had a 'Dansette' which was a very popular model.

Road   The boaters' term for the canal route. Regular boaters would 'know the road' well: where the tricky turns were, where the shallow bits were, where were the best places to tie up. A 'good' road was one with all the locks ready for you. If you were following other boats into locks and having to reset them all, it was a 'bad' road.

Shafts	The short shaft, usually with a hook on the end, was kept on the cabin roof and used for a variety of purposes, mainly to clear debris from the blades. Longer shafts (often 10 or 15 feet) were kept in the hold or along the cloths, and used to push the boat off the mud, or to assist the steerer when winding (turning).
Snatch	Boaters' word for a tug, or tow. One boat might 'give a snatch' to another that was stuck on the mud ('stemmed up'); or a motor might give another craft a snatch through a tunnel.
Speedway	Started in the 1920s, Speedway became a craze in the '50s and '60s, particularly amongst the working classes. Teams of motorcyclists raced round dirt-track courses (often at a dog-racing stadium). It featured some spectacular and daring cycling, and was both dangerous and thrilling. Most speedway tracks have now disappeared.
Stemmed-up	When a boat or pair of boats runs aground in the shallows.
Stop	A recognised place for tying up after a day's boating. Also, until tolls were done away with in the early 1960s, the place where a boat would be gauged, so that its cargo could be checked and the correct toll levied.
Summit	The highest point on a canal, or on a particular stretch of a canal, where the locks fall at each end. On a long canal, such as the Grand Union, there might be several summits.
Table Cupboard	The cabin cupboard with a fold-down front that forms a small table. The front of this cupboard is traditionally painted with a castle and decorated with roses and other flowers.
Towpath	Running continuously alongside the canal this path was originally provided for the towing animal – usually a horse or mule. The path occasionally changes from side to side, often with a 'turnover bridge' which allows the horse to cross the canal without having to detach the towing line from the boat.
Twin-tub	The latest in washing machine technology in the early 1960s. One tub contained and heated the hot water. The second was a spinner that removed most of the water from the washing, which still had to be transferred by hand. It wasn't a machine you could turn on and leave like the automatics of today.
Water Cans	Containers of varying sizes, but usually holding about two gallons of water. With spouts and handles and a hinged lid they were kept on the cabin roof near the chimney and often, though by no means always, highly decorated.
Winding	The process of turning a boat round. The word rhymes with the wind that blows. Because narrow boats of 70 feet in length cannot turn just anywhere, special wide areas known as winding-holes are provided at convenient places along the cut.
Windlass	The boatman's 'iron', a removable handle that fits onto the shaft of paddle gear to operate the locks, and is used sometimes to raise lift-bridges. The shaft sizes still vary somewhat and many windlasses today are provided with two different-sized heads.
Wireless	The original, popular name for a radio set. When transmissions first started no wires were required to be connected with the source of the broadcast – unlike the telephone and telegraph systems – hence 'wireless'. When the transistor allowed sets to be made smaller and portable in the '50s and '60s, they became more generally known as radios. You may still hear older people referring to the 'wireless'.